THIS GYNAECOLOGICAL LIFE

THIS GYNAECOLOGICAL LIFE

Columns from *The Diplomate*
&
The Obstetrician and Gynaecologist

1994-2023

James Owen Drife

Foreword by **Miss Fatima Husain FRCOG**

First published in collected form in the UK 2023

A catalogue record for this book is available from the British Library

ISBN: 978-1-85457-115-1

This Gynaecological Life by James Owen Drife
Published by:
Clinical Press Ltd.
Redland Green Farm, Redland, Bristol, BS6 7HF

Also available from Clinical Press

This Medical Life by James Owen Drife

More Autobiography/Biography from Clinical Press

*You don't have to be a genius…*By Diana Ashworth

The Dog Comes With The Practice…. by Tom Baskett (Second expanded edition!)

Resuscitation Greats by Peter JF Baskett and Thomas F Baskett

Evolution of Pre-Hospital Emergency Care, Belfast & Beyond
by John S Geddes, Ronald D Stewart, Thomas F Baskett

A Tale of Two Doctors by Sabina Skopinska, and Monika Blackwell

Sir Francis Bacon by Peter M Dunn

A History of Caesarean Birth From Maternal Death to Maternal Choice
by Thomas F Basket

Losing Eldorado : Searching for the Soul of America by Mark T Goddard

Foreword

As a current RCOG Council member and regular reader of 'TOG', I am delighted to introduce this collection of the articles entitled *'And finally'* written by Professor Drife in the Continuing Professional Development (CPD) journal of the RCOG, between 1994 and 2023.

Both as trainee and consultant, I would flick straight to this page when the journal landed on my doormat. It was supposed to provide light relief after the heavy diet of CPD in *'The Diplomate'*. The journal was renamed *'The Obstetrician & Gynaecologist'* in 1998 and then simply *'TOG'*. In the author's words, his aim was "to boldly reminisce where no one has reminisced before". True to CPD evolution, this is 'reflective practice' at its best!

The collection spans almost three decades of commentary on the evolving role of an obstetrician and gynaecologist; life as a junior on the labour ward, Calmanisation, the European Working Time Directive, and changing attitudes of consultants and trainees, as well as the speciality's and the College's vital place on the world stage. Professor Drife's leadership of the 'confidential enquiries' reports amongst other major works allowed him to travel extensively, adding to the international flavour of the book. However, his love of Scotland, singing and performing is ever present throughout.

Whether a student, trainee or senior clinician in our field, the reader will get a profound insight into history, culture, language and societal change on a background of self-deprecating Scottish humour. The intricate word play with the English language is one of the highlights of *'And finally'*. Professor Drife provides a mischievous and humorous view of the British medical culture over the decades which will make many feel nostalgic about their own training days.

'This Gynaecological life' will appeal to all obstetricians and gynaecologists, not only as a source of entertainment, but also as inspiration in their everyday practice. We are fortunate that Professor Drife has shared with us his wisdom, insight and humour in this wonderful book.

Miss Fatima Husain FRCOG MRCGP DIPM
Consultant in Obstetrics & Gynaecology, Wexham Park Hospital
Lead for Reproductive Medicine & Fertility
Associate Clinical Professor in OBGYN & Site Director for American University of the Caribbean
Fellows' Representative on RCOG Council for Thames Valley and Wessex

The Diplomate

The Diplomate, a quarterly journal founded by Prof. John Studd and published by the Royal College of Obstetricians and Gynaecologists, was aimed at general practitioners holding the DRCOG Diploma. After passing the exam they had little contact with the College, and John thought the *The Diplomate* would help them to keep up to date.

He asked me to contribute a regular column, "The Back Page", partly because my wife was a GP and partly because I'd contributed chapters to some of his books. I was already a regular contributor to the BMJ and John – like the BMJ editor – believed that a medical journal should include some light relief.

It soon became clear that Members and Fellows (MRCOG and FRCOG) also need help to keep up to date. The College has a long-standing scientific journal (the *BJOG*) but needed a new one focussing on continuing medical education. In 1998 *The Diplomate* metamorphosed into *The Obstetrician and Gynaecologist.*

JOD

The back page ....

Married to the mob

My wife is not a diplomate – at least, not of this college. Feeling that one obstetrician in the family was enough, she decided to gather her diplomas from other corners of the medical vineyard. She is now qualified to look after healthy children (why is there not a Diploma in Child Disease, I wonder?) and to lodge, when in town, in Princes Gate,[1] though I am not sure how well she sleeps next door to the former Iranian Embassy.

Two doctors in one household

As many diplomates know, life with two doctors in one household is not all beer and skittles. (If one doctor's practice does organise beer and skittles, the spouse doctor's unit is sure to have organised something else at the other end of town.) We get two sets of junk mail and, in defiance of the laws of statistics, we are both chosen out of all the people in our street to be eligible for amazing prizes. We never confuse our letters, however: they address my wife as "Dear Dr Drife" and me as "Dear Professor Frcog". As a senior house officer on the delivery suite, I used to envy the lifestyle of my consultant, who was married to a doctor and lived in a small mansion. "Leave the phone ringing if you call me, Jim", he would advise. "We shall be gardening this afternoon."

As I held the phone for the required ten minutes, I imagined him riding in from the depths of his estate on a mini-tractor in a cloud of grass cuttings. The reality for us is less bucolic. Rather than being DINKIES (double income, no kids) we are OAAHIEKS (one and a half incomes, expensive kids) and I can still reach the phone from the bottom of my garden in fifteen seconds.

1. In 1994 the Royal College of General Practitioners was located in Princes Gate, Knightsbridge, London SW7

Medical academics are not the sort of people admen bother to classify. We might be of more interest to counsellors or dietitians: they could call my wife a HADOS (husband a doctor – zero sympathy) and me a WADOS (wife a doctor – zero supper).

General practice

When I am lecturing to general practitioners I often point out that my wife is one of the brotherhood – sorry, siblinghood. I am conscious of radiating smugness when I tell them this, as if being a husband to a general practitioner gives me Associate Membership, with instant insight into the job. It does not, of course. In fact, the longer I watch my wife at work, the greater is my incomprehension. "What is general practice?" I ask myself. You attend courses every week until you know absolutely everything, and then you spend most of your working day on the telephone trying to arrange social support for other people's elderly relatives.

The most difficult thing about being husband to a general practitioner is suppressing your natural instincts. Primitive man was supposed to protect his mate from aggressors. On-call weekends were the worst time: they used to rack up the tension, with both of us picking up different extensions whenever the phone rang. What struck me about the people on the other end was that they never sounded ill. Simple, yes; bloody-minded, yes; but sick, no.

Those telephone calls gave me a chilling glimpse of a world I never knew existed. Sore throat? Runny nose? Got that rundown feeling? Request a home visit! – preferably at two o'clock in the morning. I fought a growing temptation to give callers free professional advice in fewer than three words, and the practice decided to buy a mobile phone and keep its patients.

Benefits of the group

The benefits of being married to a group are considerable, however. Before holidays I am made to submit to prophylactic injections that I would never think of asking for. My articles are intelligently edited before I send them off and, most importantly, I get advance warnings of the questions that really worry general practitioners – like "Why is there a ten-month waiting list for an ear, nose and throat appointment in your hospital?" and "Does Mr So-and-So really exist? None of the NHS patients I refer to him has ever actually seen him."

Years ago, while I was doing another senior house officer job, one of our senior registrars used to boast about having been a general practitioner. He had returned to obstetrics and gynaecology because he got tired of carrying a huge rubber torch to defend himself on night calls in Scotland's historic capital city, but he argued that a spell in general practice should be compulsory for all aspiring specialists, just as hospital jobs are part of a general practitioner's training. I suppose Calmanisation now makes it unlikely that a Diploma in General Practice will be introduced to enhance registrars' chances on the hospital career ladder. Having a general practitioner as a spouse will remain the best we can do. I expect the bureaucrats in Brussels are already thinking of making it compulsory.

The obstetric alcohol syndrome

The picture at the top of page 7 has caused a lot of comment. I chose a photo of myself and 'Er Indoors' (or more accurately, 'Er In t'Surgery') to symbolise the close relationship between general practice and obstetrics and gynaecology, but unfortunately attention has focused on what we are holding in our hands. After Council the other day the President drew me aside, his face grave, and asked me if the rumours were true. "Fellows are saying, young Drife, that you have been photographed drinking lager in public."

Protocol

Few obstetricians and gynaecologists are abstainers, but people in our position are expected to take their alcohol in style. Thus obstetricians drink gin and tonic before dinner and whisky afterwards. I can manage this tolerably well. While dining we converse knowledgeably about the wines. This gives me more difficulty. As a native of the Cotes du Clyde my experience of viniculture is limited: all I know is that the bouquet is greatly enhanced if someone else is paying for the bottle.

The other problem with wine is that it makes me thirsty. At formal dinners the organisers usually provide a bottle of English water (with a name like "Middlesex Meadows" or "Hartleigh Pool") which is quickly consumed. The waiter turns the full force of his amnesia on anyone who asks for a replacement. As the evening progresses, the dehydrating effect of the preprandial G & T is compounded by frequent sips of some excellent New World vintage – perhaps a 1985 Ayer's Rock Chardonnay, *mis en bouteille au billabong*.

If there are after-dinner speeches I reach for the port, resigned to the prospect of my metabolism taking a day to recover. If not, my pulse quickens at the prospect of sneaking out to the pub for a beer if the soiree breaks up before last orders. I am not alone. This is why from time to time the watering-hole next door to the College fills up with middle-aged men in DJs of character, who prop themselves elegantly against the fruit machine and discuss recherché aspects of colposcopy to the mingled irritation and fascination of the Baker Street regulars.

Abstinence

Back at the antenatal clinic next day, the same obstetricians will be earnestly advising their pregnant clients to give up drink. Or rather, they will be listening to midwives and junior staff doing so. Few consultants, I suspect, feel evangelical about introducing prohibition into antenatal care. I certainly do not. In two decades of working in seaports and city centres I have never seen a case of "fetal alcohol syndrome". My wife and I had our children before the idea was popularised and our two erstwhile fetuses show no stigmata from their *in utero* partying.

I am surprised at women's willingness to agree to this self-denial in pregnancy. The prospect of nine months without Tetley's would give me acute tachycardia with late decelerations. Perhaps the reality might be less distressing, however. Like other academics I enjoy lecturing in the stricter Islamic countries, where conversation can be just as convivial over strong coffee as it is elsewhere over cocktails. Curious how tipsy one can feel after one late-night Barbican.

Attitudes

Returning to Britain from these trips, I am always struck by the

10

enthusiasm with which alcohol is promoted here, and by the inconsistency of our attitudes. For example, the pretence that the English pub is out of bounds to the under-18s must be the most transparent of our many national hypocrisies. Like other parents I have learned to live with the fact that under-age drinking is now more or less compulsory among Britain's teenagers. I tried coming on strong like a cross between a Victorian paterfamilias and King Canute, but it did not work.

Those "RU18" notices are like our 30 mph speed limit signs – aspirations rather than protocols. Our drinking laws date from the age of the stagecoach. On my early-morning train journeys to London the loudspeaker tells me that breakfast is served and the bar is open, but does not explain why Intercity expects commuters to arrive at work inebriated. We do not, of course. King's Cross already has enough Scottish drunks still on the pavement.

Hospitals, though, seem more puritanical than they used to be. The managers (who all knock off at opening time) primly ban alcohol from the premises, even at Christmas. The midwives, anxious to dispel folk-memories of Mrs Gamp, are sober creatures these days. But the doctors still receive lovingly-wrapped, enticingly glugging presents from grateful patients.

I think this is because Joe and Josephine Public mistrust teetotal professionals. They like us to show common humanity with our clientele by enjoying the odd glass or two. This is a duty doctors share with lawyers and priests. Obstetricians, however, have night work to worry about. We must keep our liver enzymes constantly alert, ready to clear the bloodstream the instant the telephone rings. This demands regular practice, even on holiday, with whatever materials are available, as my picture demonstrates.

The travel page

Really important people do not travel: they materialise, unrumpled, on some new location and are then spirited away by a huddle of aides. Unfortunately, professors do not belong to this superleague. Not for us a road crew of personal assistant, minder, chauffeur, fax operator and masseuse. Instead, our academic secretary sends us off like evacuees, clutching in one hand a large briefcase and in the other a typewritten address and instructions on how to get there.

Travel essentials

Our overloaded briefcase represents a kind of professorial security blanket. It normally contains a thesis we are examining, two or three manuscripts we are refereeing, a folder of references for an article we are writing and a bundle of papers for the meeting we are attending that day. The meeting papers are the only ones we will actually read: the others are there in case the train breaks down and we panic because we have time to spare with nothing to do.

Rail manoeuvres

We do not really enjoy travel. Despite those British Rail commercials, we never kick off our shoes and curl up with Iris Murdoch. Nevertheless, we delight in being unavailable for a few hours and working, for once, to our own rhythm. If two professors are travelling on the same train they usually pretend not to notice each other; although sometimes, if they work in the same medical school, they may hold a planning meeting, this being the only chance they will have to get together that term.

On trains professors are allowed to travel first class, but this is not necessarily an advantage. Especially on the East Coast route, it may mean sitting within earshot of health economists or young men from the National Health Service Executive, who talk loudly and confidently about how to reorganise the health service. The professor slumps under a little cloud of depression, wishing that his job, too, involved merely dreaming up half-baked ideas and issuing letters telling other people to implement them.

The other disadvantage is that first-class carriages are infested by portable phone users who suffer from a compulsion to call their secretary at frequent intervals. They give a running commentary on the journey ("We are just going into a tunnel. Hello?") at the top of their voice and ask if there are any messages. There never are. The professor grits his teeth and dreams of revenge: perhaps they will give away their telephone number. He can then slip off to the toilet and use his own mobile to call them and say the computer has just sold all their shares by mistake.

International expeditions

As well as undertaking rail journeys a professor is also expected to travel abroad. These trips give National Health Service colleagues the pleasure of making pointed remarks about absenteeism and they also allow his staff to relax. As a junior academic I remember the feeling of freedom in the department when the prof was safely out of the country, and now I notice accusing glances if I stay too long in Leeds.

International travel has its own stresses. The looming date of departure becomes a deadline by which the professor must finish all overdue reports, articles and correspondence. With two days to go he checks the invitation to find out the title of his talk. To his horror he realises that his lecture is out of date. Years of academic training then show their value. He has learned how to conduct a library search in two hours flat, including photocopying, and has cultivated friendship with the medical photography department, who remain calm when asked for new slides by five o'clock. He adds these to his old faithfuls and takes three times as many slides as he needs: the final selection will be made at the last minute, depending on the mood of the meeting.

Decisions, decisions. To take or not to take the laptop computer? It is quite heavy and the professor is worried by airlines' on-board safety announcements, which now include dire warnings about the dangers of operating electronic equipment in flight. The professor takes it, switches it on apprehensively at 37,000 feet and keeps looking out of the window to check that the plane is the right way up. As the scheduled descent commences he stows it away and resolves to diet: the stewardess has had to ask whether or not his seat belt is fastened.

At the exotic foreign conference centre, the conscientious academic faces another difficult choice. Does he sit in his hotel room and work through the overfilled briefcase or does he use this opportunity to broaden his mind? He ends up trying to do both. He wakes early, does some work, goes into town, tries to find a restaurant with local colour that is not a tourist trap, fails, samples the local wine, strolls around, meets some colleagues, samples the local beer, gets lost trying to find the way back to his hotel, wakes early to rearrange his slides, and when he gets home he calls it jet lag.

13

Is there life after dinner?

The top table at a formal dinner is a very public eating-place. You have to look as if you are enjoying yourself, at least until the soup, when people stop glancing at you. It is hard, however, to appear relaxed when you have had nothing but Malvern water all through the reception and you are limiting yourself to one glass of wine before your speech. You envy the clergyman at the end of the table: once he has said grace he can throw caution to the winds.

Ideal seating plan

The unilateral seating plan at the top table means that you have no chance of seating opposite a beautiful stranger who will listen wide-eyed to a description of this morning's hysterectomy. You cannot help resenting this: after all, almost every speaker, when he stands up, is tall enough to be seen over the head of *une petite gamine* seated opposite; if he is not, he could stand on his chair. The reason for this convention is that at very formal dinners the top-table guests are on display like the silverware – there to be seen and not heard.

Spotlight on the speaker

Somewhere in every row of picturesque dignitaries, however, is a plain-looking chap without a chain of office or a row of medals on his lapel. This odd man out (it is almost always a man) is the jester and can be recognised by his glum expression. He tenses up during the main course and becomes dyspeptic over the Stilton. Why is he there, you ask? Because once, long ago, he gave a speech which made people laugh and in the underpopulated world of after-dinner speaking, a man can live down failure but not success.

Life as a speaker has its compensations, of course. You do not have to pay for your meal and you do have an excuse for refusing to put a signed banknote into the fundraising raffle. You also meet some very nice people, even if they do insist on telling you their symptoms. For me, the ideal top-table neighbour is a visiting professor's nubile research associate who does not speak or understand a word of English.

Not all speakers are so antisocial. Once I sat near a suave performer who kept his neighbours entertained with a stream of jokes all through dinner, then stood up and retailed exactly the same repertoire to the assembled multitude. For most of us, however, eating before speaking is like trial by sherry before an interview, and we have to slip out during one of the courses to commune, tight-lipped, with nature. One speaker, who is also a doctor, copes by consistently arriving halfway through the meal having been "delayed by an urgent case".

Advice to the uninitiated

Clearly, then, after-dinner speaking is a burden that should be shared among the profession rather than carried by a few perspiring volunteers. You may argue that a willingness to speak is a congenital rather than an acquired disorder. The truth is that after-dinner speaking is a craft, like surgery, which depends less on natural aptitude than on painstakingly learning the tricks of the trade.   As part of my campaign to increase the number of recruits to the craft, here are a few tips.

Like a surgeon, a speaker needs adequate light and equipment.   Do not stand in a dark corner. Do use a microphone. At the risk of bewildering the non-technical reader – a word or two about advanced microphone skills.   The instrument should be pointed towards your mouth, not your ear. It functions best when switched on. It is permissible (though unheard of at medical dinners) to identify the "on" switch *before* you start to speak. As with any operation, the opening is crucial.   The trainee surgeon is taught that the first stroke of the scalpel should be bold and confident, and the same goes for a speech. A harder lesson is that the best speakers, like good surgeons, keep their operating time short. At a conference dinner some time ago I paused for breath as I was beginning to get into my stride, and the distinguished colleague sitting beside me hissed, "Sit down!" I obeyed and my sudden disappearance provoked unusually warm applause. There are regional variations in surgical technique and also in jokes. Scots like their humour couthy – a word which I think means a mixture of "homely" and "shrewd".   Northerners are surprisingly sentimental. Ireland is replete with comic talent but generous to visiting neophytes. These differences, however, are of little importance to a speaker. Wherever he is he must follow the golden rule: be yourself.

Operating on the young is a discrete subspecialty and the same applies to after-dinner speaking.   During the day senior doctors pontificate but in the evening they like to listen. Students or juniors, by contrast, spend the day being deferential and cannot be expected to continue doing so after dinner. *"Qui est cet ancien flatus de trepannage?"* murmur these bright young things, as the older top-table guests strain to hear your speech amid the hubbub. You realise that *trepannage* means "boring" and *ancien* means "old" and you remember again the motto of medical speakers through the ages: do not give up the day job.

As ithers see us

The title is not a misprint, it is a quotation. It comes from Scotland's national bard, Robert Burns, who (according to my copy of his collected works) wrote: "O wad some Power the Giftie gie us To see oursels as ithers see us!" The argot is necessary to make it rhyme but once you know that "wad" means" would" and that "oursels" should have an apostrophe, you will understand what he is saying.

Perceptions of the medical profession

It is hard for us doctors to know how others see us. As we mutate from medical student to doctor and then, perhaps, to mister or professor, we think we understand what people's expectations are of each stereotype. But do we really? I have been trying to remember what image I had of, say, a general practitioner or a professor before I joined the medical fraternity.

It was not a productive exercise. In the Scottish mining village where I went to school we did not meet many professors. Asked as a child to describe a professor I would probably have suggested a bald, bearded, bookish man with a bow tie and a funny accent. So far, so accurate. But what about general practitioners?

Although ours was a small village it had more than one general practitioner. They all had one thing in common – they grunted. As he listened to your chest the general practitioner remained silent and then gave a non-committal grunt as he wrote something down. You tried to read something into it. Three months to live? A hopeless case? Then, suddenly, he might smile, though never for any obvious reason.

Once when Mum was in hospital, we (the children) went to lunch with Dad to the local boarding house where a new general practitioner had just taken up lodgings. He was in the dining-room, hidden behind his newspaper, and we lowered our voices respectfully. He remained silent. Eventually Dad tried to draw him into conversation. He grunted, just once, before leaving the room.

We interpreted this as a sign of depth. We knew doctors carried a heavy burden of knowledge and responsibility and we did not expect them to be happy in their work. It was to be more than a decade before I met a cheerful general practitioner. He was my tutor during my undergraduate attachment and he told me a joke. This made such a powerful impression on me that I still use it whenever I speak after dinner.

Obstetricians, of course, were unknown beings in another world. At our school we did not speak of forceps deliveries or placenta accreta. Nevertheless, I gradually became aware of the local obstetricians as individuals if not as professionals.

Teacher once asked us to state our place of birth. Most of the class had been born 30 miles away in a town called Irvine. I was intrigued. What natural disaster had befallen Irvine to cause this mass migration of refugees clutching their neonates? A tidal wave on the Firth of Clyde, perhaps, or an attack by belated Vikings?

The explanation, it transpired, was that Irvine was the home of Ayrshire's maternity hospital, then as now. (Though not, of course, in Robert Burns's time; otherwise bus loads of tourists might nowadays be surrounding it instead of that thatched cottage in Alloway.) In my youth the hospital's two obstetricians were household names throughout the county.

Local folklore raised them to the status of mythical beings. One of them was of Russian descent and according to rumour had narrowly escaped a posse of murderous Bolsheviks during the revolution. The other was blessed with a memorably droll turn of phrase and (I later discovered) a fondness for check waistcoats.

Both of them evidently understood the value of creating a character and playing up to it.

Developing the necessary character

Medical training does not prepare you for such celebrity. Eccentricity is discouraged by one's student peers and remains a disadvantage to the junior hospital doctor. A senior registrar in a teaching hospital is a chameleon who assumes by turns the characteristics of each consultant as

17

he or she moves from clinic to clinic.

Only after the final successful interview can a specialist fully develop those quirks that the public so enjoy – and which, incidentally, are important in creating what marketing men call "brand loyalty". You can be absent-minded (always good for hilarious anecdotes) or you can be a lofty patrician (like the Glasgow consultant still fondly remembered for telling a "Rab C. Nesbitt" patient: "Now, my man, you must give up alcohol: not even a glass of sherry before dinner").

The possibilities are numerous, but it is essential that each consultant's character is clear and consistent. It is no use being "lovable but disorganised" one week and "irascible but efficient" the next. This disconcerts your clinic staff and causes difficulties for your general practitioner colleagues. They need to know your public persona before they can decide which patients to refer to you and which to send to others – or perhaps ithers.

Empty nest syndrome

Our two children left home last year. To lose both looks like carelessness (as Lady Bracknell said in a different context), but our excuse is that they were lured away by institutes of higher education. They were willing victims, of course. What was less predictable was our feelings.

Having sat through many fine talks on the menopause I was familiar with the concept of the *empty nest syndrome*. Youthful lecturers cite it as a cause of climacteric depression, along with "loss of reproductive capacity", "cessation of menstruation" and "end of the parental role". I had always been sceptical that any of these could possible cause depression, but I was willing to learn by experience.

The prodromal phase

The first thing we discovered was that the empty-nest syndrome has a prodromal phase, the full-nest syndrome. Nests, you will remember, are designed for immobile chicks who squeak, feed and sleep while busy parents fly in and out, their beaks full of goodies. In the full-nest syndrome these roles are reversed. The parent birds sit squeaking in the nest while large numbers of hefty fledglings from a variety of local nests fly in and out in a preoccupied sort of way.

As the full-nest syndrome develops it is characterised by an unlinking of circadian rhythms. On the one hand, the parents are reaching the stage where the only way they can cope with rush-hour traffic and hospital managers is by getting up earlier and earlier in the morning; while on the other, the fledglings are becoming almost completely nocturnal. The nest becomes a kind of time-share.

The medical literature is of limited help with these syndromes. My wife found a book called *Living with Teenagers,* designed to help parents understand their youngsters. There are also books for teenagers, aimed at helping them to understand themselves. Books about young people's problems are all very well, but what we parents need is an understanding book about our own situation. It should be written in down-to-earth language with a humorous illustration on every page. It could start with a chapter entitled *You and your body,* which should begin:

"When you reach a certain age your body suddenly alters. Some of these changes make you feel gawky and self-conscious. Your abdomen expands so that the trousers you bought as a registrar no longer fit. Your muscles become weak. So do your eyes. You begin leaning backwards when you read things. Grey hairs start growing out of your nose."

(At this point the text would be interrupted by a cartoon of a bald man bursting out of hippie flares and falling over backwards with a rabbit peering out of each nostril.)

*"When you notice these changes, do not worry! They are entirely **normal!** They are simply Nature's way of telling you that in quite a short time you are going to die."*

Paternal self-consciousness begins subtly. Your ultra-cool timesharers point out that *nobody* wears a coloured shirt with a white collar any more. Come the weekend, they look at your cardigan with its leather buttons and smile sadly. Defiantly, you decide that you will be damned rather than change the sartorial habits of a lifetime.

A mite too anxious to avoid pretending to be hip, you over-compensate and slide towards self-parody. You refer to Radio 4 as the "Home Service" and Radio 2 as the "Light Programme". You reminisce a great deal about Beatlemania. You make no attempt to learn how to work the video recorder; indeed you really believe that this feat is physically impossible for a man of your age.

At this point, if you are an academic, you start looking uneasily at your students. For rather a long time you have assumed that you and they share an instinctive rapport. Now you realise that a generation gap has insidiously developed. Having experienced your own children's knowing but deadpan sense of humour, you become paranoid. Are your students really asking naïve questions or are they sending you up?

Characteristics of the syndrome

Then, suddenly, you and the memsahib have the house to yourselves. It feels not so much an empty nest as a ship whose engine has stopped: the accustomed throb of the life force is no longer there in the background. At first the novelty is exhilarating. You can sneak out together in the evening without leaving notes. You can pick up the phone without interrupting confidences on another extension. You can tidy up. Satisfying as they are, however, these activities are a bit short on intellectual stimulation.

When you miss most is the cross-cultural fertilisation. No longer do you feel that you are near the nation's artistic cutting edge. Over the years names like River Phoenix, Vic Reeves or The Buzzcocks would have meant nothing to you without guidance from the resident cultural attaches from the Republic of the Young. Inside knowledge meant you could do a bit of throwaway name-dropping during your undergraduate tutorials: references to Classic FM are just not the same.

Desert island discs

Dedicated as they are to the finer things in life – theatre, wine and Royal College of Obstetricians and Gynaecologists' meetings – the back pages of this journal, nevertheless, lack a column for music lovers. Perhaps this reflects a lack of consensus among the editorial board about what sort of music to review. The Editor-in-Chief, I imagine, would prefer opera, his younger colleagues would want "new wave" bands and the Scottish contingent would no doubt hold out for something that skirls.

Music is supposed to have a universal appeal but nowadays, like epidemiology, it divides us into cohorts based on age, ethnic origin and ... dress sense. I used to work in Leicester, where the De Montfort Hall, the town's biggest concert venue, lay between my home and the hospital. I would drive past different audiences of uniformly-dressed people and try to guess who was performing. Cravats and blazers – James Last? Leather – Siouxsie and the Banshees? Denim – Status Quo? Normal people – must be a sixties roadshow.

It seems that music is only part of a concert's attraction. As important is the feel-good factor of mixing with like-minded people. To that extent the modern concert has replaced the church service or political rally.

One pitfall, then of a music column, is that it exposes the writer to the contempt and ridicule of unlike-minded people. That is a risk I shall have to take, but I guess that only a minority of readers are into gangsta rap, country and western or (with due respect to my compatriots) Scottish accordion music.

At work

Another pitfall is that most *Diplomate* readers are likely to be way ahead of me in musical sophistication. One of the many advantages of being a general practitioner is that the time between house calls can be filled with sound from your car's security coded cassette player. In hospital we do not have the same opportunities to brush up on our listening, though I suppose there is nothing to stop us doing ward rounds with Walkmans. We could always leave them on during the more boring consultations.

By and large, hospitals are music-free zones, the main exception being the geriatric wards (or whatever they are called nowadays). Things may be different today but when I was a junior, elderly patients were subjected to what we would now call music abuse – the wireless blaring out Radio One from dawn till dusk. No wonder they are catatonic and doubly incontinent. When my generation reaches the age at which the ward-maid addresses us by our first names the radio will, I hope, be tuned more humanely to a golden oldies station. Can one ever tire of Beatles music? Time will tell.

Another occasionally tuneful part of the hospital is the operating theatre. Some anaesthetists feel that even though their patient is (they assure us) sound asleep, soothing tunes will reduce the need for postoperative analgesia. Scientific proof is lacking, however: what we need is a controlled double-blind (double-deaf?) comparison between those Tammy Wynette tapes and traditional live music in the form of intermittent operatic fragments from the surgeon.

21

On holiday

Before my suggestions for your winter sunshine holiday records, a few simple guidelines. You get best value from songs, which include both words and music. Poems without tunes are too intellectual and music without words is, not to put too fine a point on it, boring. The lyrics must, of course, be in English. At a stroke, then, we have excluded a large percentage of the catalogue.

As to the best examples of the songwriters' craft, the greatest exponents are still Gilbert and Sullivan. I suggest packing *Pinafore* this year – some of its observations about nineteenth century naval bureaucracy apply nicely to the National Health Service.

Two other geniuses rather neglected at present are Flanders and Swann. Take their *Bestiary* and marvel anew at its gratuitous internal rhymes for "hippopotamus".

Anything by Chuck Berry, a brilliant miniaturist whose avuncular affection for young girls shines through his lyrics.

The Flying Pickets – how can anyone not love *a cappella* singing? When *Only You* was in the charts my attempts to master the castrato line caused the resignation of a valued scrub nurse.

Bruce Springsteen's *Born in the USA* will make you feel like a houseman again. Whether you want to is up to you.

I bet it is years since you listened to *Sergeant Pepper. When I'm 64* does not seem such a long way off now, does it?

For those serious moments, take Andrew Lloyd Webber's *Requiem.* I know it is in Latin, but it still qualifies. It made Sir Andrew cry at its premiere. If it does the same to you, stop the car.

Finally, breaking my rules, an instrumental. I last saw The Shadows in the De Montfort Hall (I wore a tweed jacket). Among their Golden Greats, *Baker Street* has a guitar riff made in heaven, and what could be nicer on holiday than to be reminded of the nearest tube station to the Royal College?

Role models

Some time in the summer of 1996 I shall celebrate a quarter of a century in hospital medicine. Looking back, it seems longer. So much time wasted on quests for unnecessary knowledge. During Part 1 of the FRCS my career depended on my knowing (among other things) the nerve supply to the fourth toe. Presumably that information is still up there, occupying a valuable brain cell but recoverable only through hypnosis.

So much time, too, frittered away in pursuit of promotion. Those long evenings spent polishing the CV, with school prizes rediscovered, career aims redefined and that agonising decision about whether or not to claim that one's hobbies included skiing.

Upward mobility in medicine, as in polite society, proceeds in sudden jumps. Every so often one finds oneself, gawky and ill at ease, in the drawing rooms of one's elders and betters. The first of these quantum leaps occurs at graduation, with the self-conscious stroll into the residents' mess, home of the ultra-cool.

Becoming a consultant

The next big change is becoming a consultant. This metamorphosis is most enjoyable in a district general hospital, where people are pleased to see you. There (I am told) you are allocated your own parking space and luxurious office, and the clerks are issued with a rubber stamp on which your name is spelled correctly.

This may happen in a teaching hospital, but do not hold your breath. Nevertheless, wherever it occurs, the change to consultant jolts your psyche. As a senior registrar your main skill was an ability to anticipate your chief's wishes (however irrational) and to justify them to sceptical patients. As a consultant you are allowed – though not encouraged – to think for yourself. (Or rather, you were, until the National Health Service reforms.)

One of the first things a consultant has to get used to is the feeling of being watched. Everyone knows when your car is in the car park and recognises your footsteps in the corridor. One of the simple pleasures of consultant life is once in a while to wear crepe-soled shoes and watch people's faces as you come round the corridor.

Taking a chair

Becoming a professor is just as daunting. You tell yourself it should not be. After all, you have got used to life on that curious pedestal on which consultants are placed by staff and patients. You have stopped grieving over the fact that nurses and junior doctors no longer speak frankly to you. And yet, when you clamber onto your Chair, there it is – that familiar feeling of becoming conspicuous again.

One way of coping is to model yourself on professors you knew earlier in your career. With the benefit of hindsight, you feel almost sympathetic to them. Each had his own ways of dealing with the stresses of the job.

Professor A had everyone in fear and trembling. Pale registrars arrived before breakfast and tension rose as we waited for the ward round. If the X-rays were not in order he dashed them to the floor – an impressive sight on an orthopaedic ward. The secretary regularly fled in tears and the juniors' nocturnal efforts were mercilessly criticised. After the great man left the ward we staggered into the coffee room and Sister would say, "He's mellowed a lot".

I worked for five months for Professor B before he actually appeared on the gynae ward. Then word went round that he was going to operate. The professorial locker was opened; the professorial boots, theatre suit and dressing gown were laid out and the professorial instruments were unearthed and autoclaved. The most important of all these items, according to the oldest lecturer, was the dressing gown. Rumours grew about how fast the old man was, and afterwards we gathered round his assistant for an already embellished action replay.

Professor C spent a lot of time in London and knew the best places for breakfast around King's Cross. This, God help us, seemed a glamorous accomplishment to his houseman. His intercity lifestyle was eclipsed by jet-setting Professor D, who asked one morning to borrow a slide because he needed it for a lecture in North Carolina that afternoon.

Professor E wanted to be Vice Chancellor but had to be content with a knighthood. When we met in his office he would heave a sigh and say he wished he was back in the Hebrides. I used to try to work out the deep, Machiavellian meaning behind that statement. Now I understand. He really did wish he was back in the Hebrides.

Professor F ... but no, Professor F is still alive. I would not want him to think he is a possible role model. And if, in life's great multiple choice, I had to choose from Professors A to E? The answer, of course, would be "all of the above".

You will, OSCE, you will

Not being a diplomate myself, my first contact with the DRCOG viva was as an examiner. In those days we descended in pairs on the unfortunate candidate and talked about the first things that came into our heads. Occasionally I meet youngish doctors who remember what I asked them that day and still harbour a grudge.

Nowadays exams are changing. Essay questions have almost disappeared, despite indignant but grammatical protests from those of us who think that a professional person should have some proficiency with the written word. Multiple choice questions have survived, unfortunately. Whenever I buy a National Lottery ticket I remember the Primary FRCS: the same little boxes and the same feeling that the result is completely random.

Nowadays the clinical and viva parts of the DRCOG take the form of an "OSCE" – an objective structured clinical examination. In our undergraduate course in Leeds our students have been examined by OSCE for several years (thanks to the foresight of an academic colleague) and we (my fellow consultants and I) have become familiar with the exam's little quirks.

The Leeds experience

Our OSCE involves a circuit of "stations" spread around the out-patient department. Each is designed to test a different clinical skill or to ask a specific question. The candidate moves from one station to another at the sound of a whistle or a bell. A rather piercing whistle is blown by my secretary every 8 minutes and a bell (borrowed from one of the wards) is rung by the senior lecturer's secretary 4 minutes later. Some stations last for 4 minutes and others last for 8 minutes.

This design of OSCE tests several skills. First, it examines the ability of the secretaries to remember whether the last noise they made was with the whistle or the bell. Any failure in this part of the exam leads to swift and spectacular chaos throughout the out-patient department.

Next, it tests the ability of the examiners and candidates to distinguish between sounds which can seem remarkably similar under examination conditions. Overall, then, its main function seems to be to examine everyone's ability to be in the right place at the right time – arguably the most important attribute of any doctor.

Theoretically, however, an OSCE can simulate, in controlled conditions, a variety of clinical circumstances. It is rumoured that eventually the Membership examination may become an OSCE too. As I am not a member of the MRCOG Examination Committee, I thought I might take this opportunity to suggest some stations for the higher exam. They are designed to test a candidate's ability to function as a consultant in the modern NHS.

The new MRCOG OSCE?

Station 1: the out-patient clinic. A patient is waiting for review after a laparoscopy for pelvic pain. She is reading a paperback entitled *The Myth of Endometriosis and the Subjugation of Women.* You have 8 minutes to find the registrar's operation note and explain the findings.

Station 2: the gynaecology ward. A physician who you know is on the Distinction Awards Committee is approaching the last empty bed along with a porter, a trolley and an incontinent centenarian. In 4 minutes, explain convincingly why you need the bed for a patient undergoing tubal surgery.

Station 3: the manager's office. An enthusiastic young woman from contracting is explaining her plan to establish an outreach clinic in a fundholding practice 30 miles away. You have 8 minutes to: (1) find out which specialty she thinks you belong to; and (2) break the news *sensitively* to her that you are not a dermatologist.

Station 4: a map of an unfamiliar hospital in which you are giving a postgraduate lecture. In 4 minutes you must identify: (1) the visitors' car park; (2) the toilets; and (3) the lecture theatre *in the correct order.*

Station 5: an easy chair in front of a television set. On screen, a smug economist from the King's Fund is telling a *Panorama* interviewer why 90% of obstetric and gynaecological surgery is totally unnecessary. You have to sit on this chair for 8 minutes without damaging the furniture, the walls or the carpet.

Station 6: a microphone and a pair of headphones. Your local radio station has persuaded you to take part in a phone-in. A listener is describing how her case was mismanaged by one of your colleagues, who has the largest private practice in town. Make sympathetic noises for 4 minutes without saying anything that could land you in front of the GMC.

Station 7: an interview committee. The candidate in front of you is in an advanced stage of pregnancy. As you ask your first question her membranes rupture. Continue the interview for 8 minutes without asking a question that might contravene the Sex Discrimination Act.

Station 8: the hospital lift. You are trapped between floors with the Trust's personnel manager. You have 4 minutes to negotiate an early retirement package which will stand up after the lift doors are opened.

Nurse! Nurse!

The first nurse I ever met was Sister Hannah Owen, the woman who delivered me. Or rather, the woman to whom I was handed after what my mother subsequently described as a particularly unpleasant Kielland's rotation. (I still have difficulty buying hats but I am optimistic that, given time, the moulding will resolve.)

Looking back, I realise that Sister Owen was, of course, not a nurse but a midwife – an Independent Practitioner In Her Own Right. I cringe to think how politically unaware I was in 1947. Later she became "Auntie Hannah", my godmother. On family occasions she usually wore a shawl and sang movingly in Welsh.

Professionally, she migrated to London, spoke English and wore the dark blue uniform of a Number Seven. After graduating I called on her with some friends, all of us in need of baths and haircuts after backpacking round Europe. She lined up her staff to meet the "visiting doctors from Scotland". Those good sports gravely shook our hands, although we must have looked like extras from *Braveheart.*

Formative experiences

"People remember nurses" is an old recruiting slogan, but it is still true. We ex-patients remember our nurses because we met them at times of stress. I have a theory that my first contact with Sister Owen's starched apron on the way to the resuscitaire initiated a Freudian imprinting process. It keeps being reinforced.

First there was the district nurse who visited me as a toddler with a terrifying glass-and-metal syringe and little bottles of penicillin. Then, more positively, there was the motherly school nurse who smiled sympathetically while the school doctor, an octogenarian with half-moon glasses, peered inside our underpants.

During my student days there was the pert staff nurse who insisted on administering a preoperative suppository despite my protesting that I was an *All-Bran* addict. And the tough little Scottish sister who removed the clips and told me not to be such a wimp.

The process continues. Recently I was summoned to occupational health for a hepatitis check. My irritation vanished at the sight of the beautiful nurse practitioner at the other end of the disposable syringe. I simpered as she used me to demonstrate venepuncture. "You can practise on medical students," she told her pupil. "They never seem to refuse."

"I'm sure they never refuse *you*," said I roguishly. Her eyes hardened and I realised anew that it is a mistake to get personal when a woman is wielding a needle.

Professional relationships

The professional relationship between doctors and nurses is permanently affected by the fact that we doctors start as medical students, the lowest of the low in the hospital hierarchy. This gives nurses opportunities to be brusque, patronising or dismissive without fear of reprisal – adding another bit of imprinting. Even today I straighten my tie nervously before approaching Sister.

After qualification, the interaction becomes a heady mixture of personality traits, interprofessional rivalries and sexual chemistry. A suitable subject for a psycho-sociological thesis, it is nevertheless best documented in hospital romances with titles like *Be Still, My Bowels* or *The Constant Temperature*.

These books are popular. In Schiphol Airport, of all places, I noticed a whole book stand filled with *ziekenhuis* paperbacks. On the covers, swarthy men in low-cut theatre pyjamas gazed fiercely but thoughtfully at pneumatic yet spirited nurses. Unfortunately the standard plot – Doctor Heathcliffe meets Nurse Cathy – is becoming less relevant to this era of gender equality. Here is my suggestion to help ease Dame Barbara Cartload and her colleagues into the twenty-first century.

THE STORY SO FAR ... Demure learner nurse BRIAN JENKINS finds himself attracted to his brooding, magnetic Team Co-ordinator, SARAH SMITH. He blushes furiously whenever her searching blue eyes linger over his shapeless white tunic and tentative moustache. He notices strange yearnings provoked by the cut of her culottes and the sparkle of her nose jewellery.

But Brain is confused by the myriad emotions produced by THE DOCTORS' new partial shift system. Every day a different mysterious stranger appears. None of them seems interested in Brian or indeed anything else. Each seems more cold and distant than the last, and yet more unattainably attractive.

BRIAN asks himself desperately what is happening to him. All his life he has wanted to be a nurse. Before he was old enough to attend school he would play with his favourite present, a toy clipboard, filling in forms and distributing questionnaires to his little friends. He reorganised his playgroup into red, green and blue teams. He made his baby sister play endless games of "Managers and Personal Assistants". Her very first lisping words had been "The nurthe thupervithor can't thee you; he'th in a meeting."

Will Brian's lifelong ambitions be tossed aside because of the passions throbbing beneath the Velcro of his unisex uniform?

NOW READ ON ...

From our foreign correspondent

Dear Editor,

I hope you don't mind my sending you the copy for this month's article on a series of jumbo-size postcards. Your deadline falls at the end of my summer holiday but my wife has discovered the secret compartment in my suitcase where I normally hide my laptop. I can't write much on this first card, I'm afraid. We are sitting at a pavement café and the family are becoming suspicious, wondering why there is such urgency about sending the antenatal clinic a panoramic view of the Gare du Nord. Mum's the word!

Montmartre, Tuesday

Well, they say you are not a real gynaecologist unless you have a daughter. It is certainly an education to wander round the square here with an eighteen-year-old woman. Long-haired men of my age keep walking up to her, clutching bits of charcoal and murmuring "jolie, jolie!" Apparently they want to draw her picture. Where did she learn such composure, I wonder? Her brother and I act as her gorillas, impassive behind our shades, but she is well able to decline their offers gracefully. They retreat with formidable displays of regret and unnecessary Gallic charm.

Downhill from these artist chappies are peddlers of African artefacts. They try to interest me in sunhats in the form of small brightly-coloured plastic umbrellas worn on one's head. The family egg them on and urge me to purchase, pointing out the risks of my hairstyle in summer. My son suggests a knotted handkerchief as an alternative. Sometimes I think my children do not take me seriously enough.

Lubeck, Thursday

My SHO, who graduated here, said Lubeck is worth a visit and she was right. A mediaeval Baltic port, it was the first German town to be bombed, on the eve of Palm Sunday, in 1942. Much of it survived, or was reconstructed, and it is a wonderful warren of old buildings and thin spires. I am irritated to find that the ancient architecture reminds me of Walt Disney. I must have been at an impressionable age when I first saw *Snow White and the Seven Dwarfs.*

The family, having failed with the sun hats, insist that we all hire bicycles. They follow behind me, giggling, as we explore the alleyways. We find ourselves in the red-light district, which consists of one shop ("Erotik Videos: Entritt Frei") and three senior citizens in hot-pants and embroidered tights. Their sinister smiles of invitation, as I wobble into view, quickly freeze when they catch sight of the rest of the flotilla. I pedal past with as much dignity as the cobblestones allow.

Europe is so matter-of-fact about these things. Back in Leeds the sex workers (as they are now called) do not ply for trade in broad daylight, but lurk by night in a tree-lined street on my route to the hospital. Leeds Council has put sleeping policemen to slow the cars down, and a sign reads: "ROAD HUMPS 400 yards". I would not think of cycling along there, but when I drive past I feel a little frisson at the thought of a breakdown. Who would find me first – the RAC or the police?

Why does every city in the world have its own unique system for buying Metro tickets? We spent ages reading the small print on automatic machines and rummaging for change. In future I shall have more sympathy for bewildered backpackers on the Bakerloo Line. Once we mastered Berlin's U-Bahn, however, we whizzed with aplomb from building-site to building-site (the Reichstag is temporarily disembowelled and there are portakabins around the Brandenburg Gate).

"Checkpoint Charlie House" is now a museum rather than a place of protest, but it still has the power to grip and move its visitors. There are the beat-up cars used in escape dashes and blurry photographs of leaps to freedom. A video of the tearing-down of the wall catches at the throat. Our youngsters are absorbed: this was only 7 years ago. We do not talk, but I ask myself "What would you have done in the Cold War, Daddy?" Not a lot, I suspect.

Berlin Zoo, Tuesday

So much for decadent Berlin. When my wife and I, with memories of Lisa Minelli as Sally Bowles, suggested a visit to somewhere degenerate our children seemed horrified. Anyway, the only decadence we could find advertised in August was a transvestite cabaret and we failed to explain its appeal to our sceptical offspring. So I am writing my last card in Der Zoologischer Garten, surrounded by wholesome families of animals, uninhibited but reassuringly heterosexual. The only trouble is, they keep reminding me of Walt Disney. I must have been at an impressionable age when I first saw *The Jungle Book.*

A touch of the runes

As we sit toasting the arrival of 1997, my wife and I may not look like a couple with the second sight. Nevertheless, we are a two-person Celtic fringe – 50% Scots, 25% Welsh and 25% Cornish. If you add in our holidays in Breton gites and my time as an external examiner to the National University of Ireland, you will see how deep our roots go into Celtic culture.

Not all Celts are into the "vision thing". Many prefer to look backward, full of nostalgia for the era of Ossian and Asterix. Some of us, however, have inherited the ability to peer into the future. The view ahead is always a little misty, which is why my personal choice of lottery numbers is usually close but never exact.

Like wealth and beauty, predictive ability is exciting only to those who do not possess it. Having the second sight does not mean communing with mystic Celtic spirits like IainmacAscilh or Kirstiwarca. It merely requires an understanding of the natural rhythms that affect us all. There are described in Celtic texts such as the *Book of Kells*. Their application to doctors is set out in its medical counterpart, the *Book of Kalls*. Here are some excerpts.

Rhythm of the Week

On the morning of the first day the healer shall sit in his chariot with a brow of thunder. He shall curse other chariots and ask his gods to punish the wilful sprites of the amber and red lights. When his journey is over he shall speak softly with the virgins who are no longer his handmaidens but who, moved by pity, may minister to him with the life-restoring infusion of the beans of the red mountain.

By the tenth hour the healer shall feel better, but then he shall receive his first visitation from the chirruping spirit of Vodafona – she who never tires of speaking. She will not be silent during the great counsels of Flipchartor, the king of the hospital, nor even on the healer's midday feast on the bread that is triangular.

Thus the healer's week shall pass, like all the others, according to the immutable laws of Jobplan. On the morning of the fourth or fifth day the healer shall meet his apprentice, Rosterdamus, as decreed by the shift that is partial. Then shall the healer talk of the old days, when his apprentice walked with him throughout the week …

Rhythm of the Year

Verily, the seasons change but the cycle remains the same. As the year begins, the manager, Dirtitrix, shall say:

"Lo, the winter is upon us and the sound of coughing is throughout the land. The beds of all the healers are needed for the old folk whose urine runs freely from them. And it will remain thus until the buds are again on the trees."

So the healers shall spend all the days of the winter in counsel, generating great heat. The wiser ones will depart and go far away into the mountains, above the line of the trees. There they shall rise in chairs and descend fearlessly on the runs men call black.

After the spring equinox there shall begin the first of two short seasons when the healers can practise their art. There shall be money abroad in the land and the beds shall be dried out. The healer shall smile and look forward to his holidays.

The summer shall begin with a great rite of passage for the young who have sat at the healer's feet. The young men shall have haircuts and the women put on their finest garments and all shall pass trembling before the healer and the elders. And the healer shall wonder at their youth.

In the eighth month the land shall fall silent and even the spirit Vodafona shall not chirrup, for the people shall go to the lands of the sun. Then in the ninth month shall come the great migrations of the healers, moving like herds of deer over the lands, from conference to conference, with their names writ small on their breasts.

As the days shorten the second brief season of healing shall arrive. There shall be peace in the land for the manager Dirtitrix shall take an off-season break beside the Ocean of the Indies. But there shall be a shadow over the healer. Each year, two weeks earlier than the last, Dirtitrix shall cry:

"Behold, the gold is gone from the coffers. O healers, I beseech you, go again to the runs men call black and do not return until blossom covers the trees."
...

The second sight

So, with a basic knowledge of these and other cycles we can predict the future with reasonable certainty. You can see why the second sight is a mixed blessing and why we Celts greet the New Year by turning to strong drink. Cheers!

The really motoring page

We held a small celebration recently when my car completed its first 125,000 miles. What I had really wanted to enjoy was the milometer reading 123456 but at the crucial moment the beauty of the Tadcaster by-pass distracted me and, by the time I remembered, the figure had passed. Like Halley's comet, it will not come again in my lifetime. Still, the demi-semi-half-million merited a couple of glasses of Kaliber.

I used to think it was necessary to change one's car every five years or so. It seemed a hygienic thing to do, like wearing clean socks and underwear every morning. A minicab driver re-educated me about cars while reinforcing my prejudice about socks. My current motor, hand-crafted from a single block of Bavarian steel, seems set to run forever.

Every few months I feel a whim to change but I cope by taking her to the car wash. She emerges gleaming and I fall in love all over again. It is, however, a mature, clear-sighted affection. West Yorkshire has one of the highest rates of car crime in England and, after all those miles, I can park in quiet side-streets with an easy mind. Indeed, when I am having one of my whims, I might leave the doors unlocked and a notice "NICE LITTLE GOER" on the dashboard.

Growing old gracefully

My first car was an Austin bought cut-price from my father. It developed chassis-rot and eventually a trusted garage-owner refused to give it an MoT. "Sorry, doctor, but I asked myself, 'Would I take my own children out in it?'" I obtained a certificate from a less scrupulous establishment and sold the car to a couple of pensioners. Years later they recognised me in the street. The man called out, "You're the doctor the doctor who sold us that 1100!" I stared at him as he limped over to me. "Put it there, doctor. Best car I ever had".

After that I went in for big models, in size if not in price. I know what Freudians would say, but my excuse was a growing family. We needed something with enough room for a guitar and a fortnight's supply of disposable nappies on our annual expeditions to French gites. Nowadays manufacturers have found ways of glamourising this stage of one's life. Barratt homes, it seems, can only be reached by 4x4 off-road expedition vehicles with bull bars and satellite navigation systems.

The age of a car can be disguised by careful maintenance and a personalised number plate, but the age of the driver is not so easily hidden. The real give-away is the presetting of the radio. Having tried Radios One, Two and Four over the years, I have now settled on Radio Three. There is something deeply pleasurable about pumping up the volume and driving past inner-city drug-dealers with atonal music plinking and clicking through one's open windows.

Doctors' cars

Reading over what I have written, I wonder if these revelations are too personal. Some things should remain taboo and one's motoring life is not a subject to be discussed in public. Nevertheless, our feeling of privacy behind the wheel is illusory. We doctors are being watched as we swing into the car park each morning and nothing defines our character more publicly than what we drive. Fashions in automobiles, like clothes, change over the years. What body shell should a caring medic wear in the nineties?

The classic doctor's car was the 1950's Rover. Bulbous and British, it exuded rectitude, financial stability and social standing. It was perhaps the Volvo of its day, but modern Scandinavian cars are a little too cool to inherit its tweedy mantle. Today's empathic family doctor needs a car which shows emotional qualities without actually breaking down. Any French marque has the right combination of torque and *sympathie*.

For the hospital doctor, sports cars are excusable at the extremes of one's career – as an SHO or an A+ award holder. For the rest of us the choice is more limited. Gone at the days when consultants drove Rolls Royces. Nowadays, even if you find a Roller driver wearing a tie, you suspect he has a gold medallion under his shirt.

Gynaecologists, more than most doctors, need to project respectability but we must also convey a hint of raffishness – a faint hint of youthful indiscretions which still bring a blush to some senior nurse's cheek. Large German cars are a popular choice but they err on the side of caution. Better to buy British. Despite sharing newsreel shots with John Major, the Jaguar has not quite lost its "cad's car" feel. Elegant lines and a bit of oomph: what better image for a gynaecologist? Sadly for professors, however, too much style would destroy our credibility. This is why most of us stick to low-profile Japanese jobs. Actually, anything will do for us provided it has at least 100,000 miles on the clock.

Songs on the fringe

Our house is slowly filling up with self-instruction books. My wife's contributions include *Russian for Beginners, Das Bayerische Kuchbuch* and *Feminist Gardening.* On my shelves are *The One-Minute Manager,* Ian Allan's *Trainspotting for the Presbyopic* and – unexpectedly perhaps – *Teach Yourself Songwriting.*

I bought my songwriting manual many years ago while preparing a student revue. At medical school it was my good fortune to be in the same year as some gifted musicians (now frittering away their talents by working as hospital consultants). This meant that our undergraduate shows were a cut above the average, with the stage filled by brass players while I doubled as lyricist and maraca player.

Soon I realised that my lyrics, not to mention my maracas, were inaudible against such an accompaniment. (In those days, banks of amplifiers were beyond the mean of student bands.) I felt a heady sense of liberation. There can be no happier training for a young songwriter than to be allowed to rhyme "moon" with "catheter balloon", serene in the knowledge that the audience cannot hear a word he is singing.

Early struggles

Songwriting proved curiously addictive. Perhaps it was the applause, although I knew that was mainly for the trombone obligatos. Perhaps it was the persistent feeling that the next song would be better. However neatly the words fitted, there was usually something missing – the spark that changes an exercise in verbal dexterity into a phrase that touches the listener's emotions.

Or perhaps it was the promise of riches. Songwriters feature on the list of the world's wealthiest people. After graduation I discovered that Walter, my co-houseman on the medical professorial unit, played a mean keyboard and composed music. We settled down to emulate Lennon and McCartney. My own muse, however, remained wedded to Flanders and Swan. To this day I feel guilty when I look across the piano at Walter. With a less polysyllabic collaborator he might be a millionaire.

Nevertheless, in the 1970s, inspired by Agnetha, Bjorn, Benny and Anna-

Frijd, we recorded an entry for the Eurovision Song Contest. It didn't win – but imagine if it had. Abba have now retired, leaving their songs to tribute bands with names like "Bjorn Again". Would we have inspired groups to call themselves "Walterations" or "Drife after Death"? We shall never know, but we console ourselves by looking at Abba now and telling each other that money doesn't bring happiness.

With hindsight we can see that we devoted too much energy to medicine and did not take our songwriting seriously enough. Recent television biographies of the big timers reveal them as driven people. Melvyn Bragg's *South Bank Show* about the Bee Gees, for example, showed that despite their white suits they are single-minded professionals.

Still, we had some good times. Most of our shows on the Edinburgh Festival Fringe were kindly reviewed. The best, looking back nearly twenty years, was "Funnissimo!", the musical of the *Guinness book of Records*. It included our only punk rock song, and some dialogue that would be impossible today. Near the beginning, Anne, our leading lady, asked if there were any dirty bits in the book. "No," I replied, "'Sex' isn't in the index. It goes direct from "sewage" to "shaft". After the 1979 edition the editors added "sex ratio" and "sextuplets", ruining the joke.

Never too late?

Now that Walter and I are reaching for the HRT, we grumble that songwriting is perceived as part of youth culture. Although Phil Collins is almost as bald as I am and Barry Manilow is older than either of us, their work seems to radiate nostalgia rather than celebrate maturity. Even in countries like Ireland where older people sing, they generally retail traditional ballads, not their own compositions.

We prefer the era – not so long ago – when songwriters looked and behaved like bank managers. People like the Gershwins or Sammy Cahn managed to combine creativity with a middle-aged lifestyle. And they valued lyrics almost as much as tunes. According to legend, when someone remarked that Richard Rogers had written *"Old Man River"*, Mrs Oscar Hammerstein replied, "Richard wrote, 'Dah, dah, da-da'. *My husband* wrote "Old Man River"".

We have not lost hope that those days will return. Nor have we stopped writing songs. Our latest collection will be discreetly unveiled on this year's Fringe, when we share a lecture theatre with Gerard Kenny, a New

York singer-songwriter of proven ability.   Are we worried about the comparison? Of course. But at our age it is rather exhilarating to feel fear. And, anyway, we think our songs are funnier than his.

"Gerard Kenny and Abracadabarets at the College" is at 7.30pm, 16-20 August, at the Royal College of Physicians, Queen Street, Edinburgh. Tickets from the Fringe Box Office.

The rock and roll years?

A fiftieth birthday used to be something to keep quiet about.   But things are different today – we baby boomers have gone through life making each of our milestones fashionable, from teenage hippiedom in the 1960s to middle-aged materialism in the 1980s. And now it's cool to be wrinkly. Nevertheless, I shall not be throwing a party. For a Scot, reaching the half-century may be a milestone, but it is no reason to toss money away, particularly with two students in the family.   I must admit that their youthful lifestyle fills me with envy. I don't remember having such a good time when I was 20, despite all the hype about the "swinging sixties". But why rely on my memory?   Even the Back Page should be evidence-based, so I checked up on a diary that I kept, briefly, 30 years ago. It seems to have been written by a complete stranger.

A vanished world

Parts of the diary make 1967 seem very far away.   On New Year's Day I summed up the state of the world: "£1 consists of 20 shillings; *The Times* is still independent; World War III still hasn't occurred; no man has landed on the moon; computers are still our servants; and I still haven't written my physiology essay." In February the Soviet Premier, Mr Kosygin, swept past on a state visit "in a Rolls Royce followed by a line of Austin Princesses". In May the price of *Punch* rose to two shillings. In September Harold Macmillan on television recalled a padre's prayer: "Lord, as it is partly through Thy efforts that we have been victorious …". Our home at that time was near the River Clyde and in 1967 ships were still built there. A local plumber who had worked in the yards told me how… "A thief was thrown 100 feet from a ship and pelted with large nuts as he swam away." On 20 September the Queen came to launch a liner known cryptically as "Q4". What I remember now is a catch in her voice as she said, "I name this ship *Queen Elizabeth the Second*". What I noted at the time was that the fly-past went over our house and that most people had expected the vessel to be called *Princess Margaret*. After all, there already was a Queen Elizabeth. Local newspapers decided the name, "*QE2*" was an insult to Scotland, which had never had a Queen Elizabeth the First.

Preclinical horrors

Thirty years on, the horror of the preclinical course remains vivid.
7 March "Very brainy lecturer – mastered the lecture theatre lights in only thirty minutes."
9 May "Today's practical class involved snipping the tails of mice infected with sleeping sickness, etc., to make films of their blood. One student was bitten. The demonstrators looked on with unfeeling glee: 'There's no literature about whether this strain is pathogenic to man and we're looking for post-mortem material'".
10 May "Umpteenth lecture about the life-cycle of the malaria parasite. Judging by the amount of time given to various subjects we shall spend our careers treating phenylketonuria, malaria, cancer and spinal cord transections, in that order, in any free time we get from administering sulphonamides."
13 December "Shown Dr Haggis's electron microscope, the only one in the medical school that isn't incapacitated in a high wind, as it is built over an archway". One could ponder that sentence for a long time.

Hello gynaecology

In July I started my first hospital job, as an auxiliary. Felix, the orderly who introduced me to theatre, was a German prisoner-of-war who had stayed on. In my hazy recollection he looks like Walter Matthau. On day two a consultant discovered I was a medical student and I was taught to scrub up. "They're exceedingly careful about sterility", I noted ungraciously. My first hysterectomy was interrupted when I touched Felix's tunic. "I have the feeling I didn't impress the doctors – they are lordly figures, of course, even their chat and profanity being different from ordinary mortals."

I remember moments of the operation, but the most vivid impression was left by the consultant – the first gynaecologist I had ever seen. After operating, he changed into a suit with a waistcoat which had a slightly different check from the jacket. Thirty years on, I still lack the nerve to emulate his epileptogenic style.

My early hospital career coincided with my learning curve as a self-taught motorcyclist and was cut short when I fell off: "The Consultant Radiologist says I do have a cracked scaphoid after all. So I had to report to a chuckling matron and have had to leave."

Nowadays, apparently, the death rate from motorcycle accidents is higher at age 50 than at 20, as menopausal men attempt to recapture their lost youth. If they had kept a diary they wouldn't bother.

Blue Train

"Great railway journeys of the word" is a phrase that conjures the exotic; but, when I was a child, all railway journeys seemed great. There was that great big leather strap for letting down the window; those landscape photographs above the seats in the compartments; those flying cinders, which had many a Trevor Howard tending the eye of many a Celia Johnson; and, of course, steam locomotives – magnificent, living machines, full of character. Wonderful for trainspotters, but when you are actually inside the train the beauty of the engine is lost on you. What really matter are the quality of the scenery and the availability of ginger beer in the dining-car.

Best of British

Trains are still my favourite transport and Britain's best journeys are those that bring glimpses of the sea – or, better still, bring the train worryingly close to the water's edge. Sit on the left hand side when you go to Torquay: after Exeter the carriage seems amphibious. Sit on the right on the way from York to Aberdeen – a trip that always stirs the blood. You teeter beside cliffs, make spectacular crossings over the Tyne, Tweed, Forth and Tay, and catch evocative glimpses of York Minster, Durham Cathedral and Lindisfarne. Even Montrose harbour seems magical.

The only imperfection on the east coast route is that so many passengers are only there for the ride. Scotsmen in a hurry take the plane. A Great Railway Journey should have serious passengers on important business and stewards working as if their livelihoods were at stake. This is what I like about Eurostar. It is not a toy. Its staff know that if they do not deliver, their customers will fly, despite the horrors of Heathrow.

On the Continent

I thought the French Train Grand Vitesse was the same but – at least when we slid out of the Gare de Lyon last year – it too was full of tourists. On the plus side, it was refreshingly free of Jobsworths. All my previous continental journeys had involved confrontations with ticket collectors brandishing "Les Regulations". The language varied but the message was always the same.

"Je regretted, Monsieur, ce billet n'est pas valid. Aujourd'hui ees a Wednesday and zees ticket say Donnerstag. And zere is an "R" in ze month. So you 'ave to pay a surcharge, immediatement. And also a fine because your ticket, he has no stamp on him".

These encounters would bring out the Briton in me. In seething Esperanto I would ask how we were expected to know all this, point to the inside front cover of my passport (*Her Britannic Majesty requests and requires …*) and warn that the Foreign Secretary was a personal friend and would send a gunboat. This cut little ice in the Alps. Better, I found, to insist on paying my fine with my most obscure credit card.

The Blue Train

All this railway experience was eclipsed recently by a trip on what the brochure claims is "the best train in the world". The Blue Train runs from Pretoria to Cape Town (and, less frequently, to Victoria Falls). You have to book months in advance, so the painful memory of the price has faded by the time you travel.

There is Buck's Fizz at the station and your luggage is taken away, airline style. The carriages are stunning – walnut panelling, brass fittings and cabins like hotel rooms, with en suite shower and a personal video ("Welcome, Professor and Mrs Drife"). On one TV channel is the view from a camera at the front of the train.

A legend since the 1930s, the train has recently been rebuilt, refurbished, restaffed by a multiracial team and relaunched with an inaugural trip by

41

the President and a bevy of supermodels and celebrities. In the cocktail lounge the barman mixed immaculate Martinis and answered our questions. President Mandela drinks dry white wine; Archbishop Tutu drinks rum and coke. We forgot to ask about Naomi Campbell.

Outside, track and railway buildings are protected by razor wire. We passed shanty towns, some upmarket, some not. When we stopped at Kimberley to peer down the "Big Hole" – the former diamond mine – there was a red carpet at the station. There were also resigned groups of black people waiting for less sumptuous transport.

When we reboarded two hours later they were still there. As our train began to move, one or two waved. We began waving to all. One man, grinning broadly, raised his middle finger in salute. We smiled back – we felt we deserved it.

An obstetrician's diary

The diaries of my fellow Yorkshireman, Alan Bennett, are best sellers. Good for him, say I. I have respected him for many years, ever since a houseman colleague performed the sermon from *Beyond the Fringe* in a Christmas pantomime. To my surprise, Bennett's subtle send-up of an English vicar ("And Esau was an hairy man…") had the Scottish hospital staff stamping and cheering.

Nevertheless, I feel a twinge of jealousy. Obstetricians lead much more interesting lives than writers and our commonplace books should be more marketable. Or they could be, if any of us kept one. So I have decided to restart my diary after a gap of thirty years. This time I shall aim at publication, which means dropping lots of famous names (while still, of course, respecting patient confidentiality.)

Friday 23rd

At dinner in the College, I sit close to Sir Naren. As the wine flows and the rest of us become more garrulous, he becomes wiser and more articulate – a splendid characteristic in an office-bearer. Peter Milton proposes a toast to James Wyatt, the long-dead vice-president who bequeathed Council this annual feast in his memory. Without notes, Peter gives a beautifully constructed speech and I am lost in admiration. Personally, I always become tongue-tied unless I have at least one sheet of paper on the table. My worst nightmare is Michael Parkinson's encounter with Rod Hull and Emu.

James Wyatt was a consultant at St Thomas's Hospital and he used to be driven around London in a Rolls-Royce. How times have changed. Nowadays the image-conscious doctor rides a bicycle. Apparently Wyatt was universally loved because he attended all the matches of the hospital rugby team. That would be too high a price for me, I'm afraid.

Back in my room after a nightcap, I call my wife on my mobile. She says I sound indistinct and I tell her it is because of my position relative to the transmitter. I find she has bought tickets for Opera North tomorrow night and I try to sound enthusiastic. But on a Saturday night, after the intellectual cut and thrust of debate in Council, I expect to feel mentally and physically drained.

Saturday 24th

Back in Leeds, just as we are about to leave for Sweeney Todd, the demon barber of Fleet Street, the phone rings. A courtesy patient, the Reader in Phrenology (name changed), has been admitted in early labour. I pick up my pager, switch it to vibrating mode and put it in my trouser pocket. If I were in private practice I would tell the theatre manager my seat number and arrange to be called during the second act, but the silent bleep has put paid to that. The only trouble is, when it goes off your first thought is that you have become incontinent.

We are in the back row of the upper circle and nobody else is wearing evening dress. As usual, Opera North's performance is terrific. The principals, Steven Page and Beverly Klein, get laughs from the clever lyrics (no mean feat) but I do wish Stephen Sondheim were a little less smart and a little more melodic. On the way home we visit the hospital. Why is the car park completely full at 11pm? The midwife looking after the Reader is clearly no enthusiast for obstetric intervention, so I should have a peaceful night. Nor does she think much of epidurals, though the same cannot be said for the Reader.

Sunday 25th

Suddenly, at 6am, I sit bolt upright in bed. This is the Reader's second baby and she should have delivered by now. I phone in but the labour ward supervisor tells me that the midwife has put up a "Do Not Disturb" sign and nobody can hear anything. I get dressed and phone again, to find that the baby has arrived.

The ability to diagnose the second stage by telepathy while sleeping is a knack that comes with age and, unlike my mobile, works at a distance. Once when I was sunbathing beside the South China Sea I felt an urge to go back to my hotel room and phone home. A surprised midwife confirmed that the Marchioness of Bradford (name changed) had just started pushing. I sent my best wishes but I gather she was not impressed.

What do you think so far?

Looking back over my first three days I doubt whether this diary will make my fortune in the bookshops. Too discreet to compare with Allan Clark and not enough blood, so far, to attract readers from Andy McNab. Perhaps I could persuade Dame Thora to read extracts on Radio Four.

Seven ages at the movies

The Diplomate carries theatre reviews but cinema is much more popular, according to Government statistics. (*Social Trends* gives figures for the population broken down by age and sex, though admittedly it does not mention doctors specifically.) These days any cultured person is expected to be, if not word perfect on the latest issue of *Empire,* at least able to tell Jeff Goldblum from Whoopi Goldberg. As modern fiction disappears up its own pretentious nostril, films have replaced books as our shared art form, appealing simultaneously to all heights of brow.

So I feel I should offer a page of movie criticism. My only reason for hesitating is that I have not been inside a cinema since 1969, except when I entered a multiplex near Glasgow to ask directions and buy Irn Bru. I feel guilty about this, like a lapsed churchgoer, but I think it is just a phase I am passing through. My cinema life can be divided into seven ages.

The child

As a kiddie I was awestruck by the power of the big screen. When Captain Nemo died at the end of *20,000 Leagues Under the Sea* despite surviving the attentions of the giant squid, I was inconconsolable. I identified completely with every hero, whether Alan Ladd in a suit of armour, Kenneth More in artificial legs or Charles Hawtrey in a policeman's helmet. This affected my behaviour for days after each film, though when I fell in love with Muriel Pavlow I knew it was forever.

The teenager

Luckily, my teens coincided with the golden age of cinema. *A Hard Day's Night* was the greatest film ever made, with a soundtrack that still thrills and a totally fantastic script. (…"Y' what?"… "I come from a long line of electricians"…). *Lawrence of Arabia* was totally fantastic, and had the greatest telephoto shot of a camel in cinema history. Then came *Dr Zhivago,* the greatest film ever made, in which Julie Christie was totally fantastic …

The student

Entering the sophisticated world of Edinburgh University meant long scarves, haggis for luncheon and my first chance to get close to cinematic demigods. James Robertson Justice (role model for all consultants as Sir Lancelot Spratt) was Rector and occasionally gave students lifts in his gull-wing Mercedes. The ill-fated Ian Charleson, long before *Chariots of Fire,* starred in a student revue. And the film society was run by utter smoothies.

I didn't join. This spared me the works of Andy Warhol but left me embarrassingly untutored in the language of cinema. On my elective in the USA, when I saw Woody Allen on stage in *Play It Again, Sam,* I had no idea who this Bogart chap was, whose image kept being projected onto the backcloth. Incredible, I know, but remember this was 25 years BC (Before Cable).

The junior doctor

Graduation brought the first pangs of disillusionment with cinema. After a week of nights in Accident and Emergency my idea of escapist entertainment did not include designer violence or in depth studies of psychopathy. What I needed was Ealing comedy but this was temporarily out of fashion. Occasional glimmers of light came in the form of *Cabaret* and *Emmanuelle.* According to my *Halliwell's Companion*, Sylvie Kristel is now forty-six. I shall not repeat what it says about Muriel.

The parent

A father's instinct is to protect his family, and it is a pity that our reproductive phase coincided with the arrival of foul language on the soundtrack. This spoiled the cinema for me but not, of course, for my children. It was I who was shocked to find that *Four Weddings and a Funeral* opens with a string of four-letter words, which even feature in *A Fish Called Wanda,* despite the presence of that wholesome Mr Palin.

The airline passenger

Nowadays the busy academic catches up with recent movies on intercontinental flights. The impact is not the same – something to do with the screen being at the far end of the cabin, the flesh tones being purply-green and the dialogue including announcements about duty free shopping. Mr Bean takes this in his stride but Mrs Brown was less impressive: its close-ups of Billy Connolly trying to look introspective were particularly unconvincing.

The couch potato

Apparently we are on the verge of an era when you can loll on the sofa at home with your zapper and call up any movie at any hour. The millennium will bring wall-to-wall Alastair Sim to those of us who want it, with Nicam Sensurround. That I should live so long! Wait for me, Muriel, I'm on my way.

Town and country music

Like many of my consultant colleagues, I am a country boy at heart. Or rather, I was. The southern uplands of Scotland where I spent my childhood are the most open of open spaces, and there was hardly a house between our back door and Newcastle upon Tyne, a hundred miles away. The bleak moorland was no tourist destination but it was a privileged environment for us small boys, and we knew it. We felt superior to unfortunates cooped up in towns and to effete lowlanders surrounded by fields and hedges. How twee, we thought. Once a year we ventured into Glasgow, on a coach trip to the pantomime, during which Kenneth McKellar would sing nostalgically about cottages in the Highlands. We understood how he felt.

The downside of rural life became obvious after puberty, when the search for a mate involved increasingly more desperate trips by bus and then – thanks to Dad – by borrowed family car. What country life gives to the teenager is a powerful motivation to get away as quickly as possible and never return.

Rural idyll

For thirty-four years I have worked in cities, not so much from choice but because this is where the medical schools are. Nevertheless, I still think of myself as a temporary visitor – and our house is on the very edge of Leeds. Of an evening, within minutes we can be in one of a number of ancient, stone-built inns, where amiable locals wear woolly pullovers.

These gnarled characters gaze into their pints of Black Sheep and mutter enigmatically to one another. If you try to eavesdrop you catch phrases like "Bangkok airport was hell, as usual", or, "I made 200K on those preference shares, ba goom." Then you remember that the car park is full of gleaming 4x4s and realise that the clientele's tans are the result, not of hours atop a combine harvester, but of a spot of R&R on the Pacific rim.

Last week we drove further afield in search of Olde England. The setting sun glowed on the Yorkshire cornfields and we stopped at The Crown, Boston Spa. Deep in the country, folks make their own entertainment and in the back room the Yorkshire Post Jazz Band was in full flow. This was wonderful. We may have been searching for a rural idyll but we had not expected to find it. The grey-haired musicians were full of that self-deprecating humour that is *de rigeur* among British jazzmen, from Humphrey Littleton downwards. They asked if the audience, like them, remembered Nissen huts and ATS girls. And stocking tops? They mopped their brows as the fans banged their zimmer frames in approval. The band launched into South Rampart Street Parade and we thought – yes, there's nothing to beat country life.

47

London living

For the medical academic, however, life is divided between home, hospital and London. "Three addresses always inspire confidence, even in tradesmen", according to Lady Bracknell, and for the last decade my pied à terre in town has been the Royal Society of Medicine. "Round the back of John Lewis's, right guv?" as the cabbies say.

I have found that things in the metropolis and in Yorkshire are not so very different. Take taxi drivers, for example. Although London cabbies are traditional Eastenders and those elsewhere are more ethnically diverse, they all share similar characteristics, with the same broad-brush approach to geography ("It's somewhere round here, mate") and the same love of excruciating phone-in programmes on local radio.

Or take the pubs. Round the corner from the RSM is the Cock and Lion, where the late evening atmosphere of peace and quiet is more reminiscent of a country inn than the heaving café-bars of central Leeds. What marks it out as a typical London hostelry is the fact that the barmaids are all from Eastern Europe (where have all the Australians gone, I wonder?).

As well as being a relaxing local it has a touch of the exotic, as customers often wear evening dress and carry violin cases. A few doors away is the Wigmore Hall, with nightly chamber music. Recently I spent a delightful couple of hours there, enjoying the youthful talent of the all-female Nossek String Quartet and violinist Christine Sohn, with Julian Milford caressing the keyboard.

It was my first visit to the hall and I had expected an audience of sensitive, willowy aesthetes like myself. Instead, I found I was sitting among a coach party of ladies of a certain age from somewhere in the suburbs. The quiet passages were accompanied by the unwrapping of bonbons lentissimo e forte, but the performers did not seem to mind. They did not talk to the audience and there was no banging of zimmer frames but, as far as pleasure was concerned, it was as good as The Crown.

Guidelines! Guidelines!

These days, most documents we receive in hospital are written by committees. Even those that aren't still aspire to the same impersonal literary style. Clinical guidelines are no exception, but what makes them unique among the papers on our desks is that we are expected to read them.

The Back Page Creative Writing and Punctuating Executive Committee (CWAPEC), anxious to raise standards of patient care, wants to help make guidelines more readable. We invited professional journalists to submit drafts which will show the Royal Colleges how medical prose might be improved. The excerpts have been anonymised for contractual reasons.

Guideline 1:
THE OBSTETRIC FLYING SQUAD
(By the staff of H*llo! magazine)

When you are called out on the Flying Squad, remember that you are being invited exclusively into a patient's beautiful home. Here are our answers to the questions you are bound to ask:

Q: *What should I wear?*
A: We recommend a blue pyjama suit with the logo of your hospital (or more commonly, someone else's hospital) stamped on the bust. Make sure it has a halter neck, as a V-neck is unsuitable for those embarrassing positions you may have to adopt in the ambulance.

Q: *What if there is blood on the carpet?*
A: We recommend WIZZO rug cleaner for those hard-to-remove stains, though nowadays the photographer can do wonders with an airbrush after the snaps are taken.

Q: *What if the patient is seriously ill?*
A: Always have one of those marvellous paramedics with you. They are very knowledgeable and they do enjoy a crisis. This more than compensates for their dress sense (they favour luminous green which is why we recommended blue for you).

Guideline 2:
TALKING TO YOUR NEW SHO
(by the staff of the E*rop*an)

1. Quand votre nouveau SHO arrive sur le ward, le premier chose a faire est decouvrer quelle langue il/elle parle. Alors, suivez nos instructions: Dites: "Bonjour, Wilkommen, Buon' giorno, Hoe gatt her met u? Nous sommes enchante de vous voir, especialement après le dernier locum, qui etait totalement inutile et sans espoir."
2. Presque certainement le nouveau SHO repondera, en parfait Anglais: "Good morning. My name is Klaus and I am delighted to be in your beautiful hospital."
3. Ne mentionez pas la guerre.

Guideline 3
FERTILITY GUIDELINES
(by the staff of G*rd*ner's W*rld)

1. Don't attempt to propagate until April. Before then, you risk frost damage.
2. One week beforehand, cover the bed with a thick layer of horse manure.
3. Stand against a south-facing wall, sheltered from the wind.
4. If no growth is seen by mid-July, try once more in the autumn.

Guideline 4
UTERINE SOUNDING
(by the staff of Ant*ques T*day)

The technique of sounding the depth of the uterine cavity varies according to the age of the instrument used. The first step is to estimate this to the nearest decade.

Most uterine sounds currently used in British hospitals were manufactured between 1920 and 1935 but some date from Victorian times. Nobody has ever seen a new uterine sound and therefore many gynaecologists believe an antique instrument is essential.

Although the case never came to trial, it is known that during the 1970s a brilliant but unscrupulous North Country metallurgist made counterfeit Edwardian sounds which are virtually impossible to tell from the real thing. His technique of mimicking the effects of repeated autoclaving on soft metal continues to baffle soundologists in Europe and America.

Details of how to estimate the age of genuine sounds will appear in a full colour 26-part magazine, *Sounds Historical,* to be published in fortnightly instalments. Part one, *From Sumer to the Pharaohs,* is in all good newsagents now.

Guideline 5
HOW TO OPEN A FILING CABINET
(by the staff of the soaraway S*n)

Pfwoar! We all love watching secretaries opening filing cabinets. Especially the bottom drawer! You may think you can't do the same but REMEMBER – the wiggle isn't necessary!!

*Step 1. **Face** the cabinet. (**EXPERT'S TIP**: For Step One, we keep our arms hanging loosely by our sides with our knuckles resting lightly on the carpet.)

Step 2. Can you see any **handles?

***Step 3. No? Look round the corner. Some cabinets have drawers on the side! (Confused? *Don't blame us,* we didn't design them!)

****Step 4. **Attach** your hand to ONE of the handles. (**It doesn't matter which arm.**)

*****Step 5. Now – **PULL!**

Easy, isn't it? So far! DON'T MISS next week's **Advanced Guideline,** for the complicated questions, like *Which handle should I pull?* or *What if there's a drawer sticking out already?*

Over to you

CWAPEC has pointed the way forward. Now it is up to the RCOG Guidelines Committee to follow.

The Obstetrician and Gynaecologist ("TOG")

1998   2023

By 1998 Continuing Medical Education (CME) had become deadly serious and highly organised, and although my column was retained under a new name ("*And Finally*"), hints were dropped that I should ease up on the frivolity. This wasn't difficult, as I'd entered my fifties and was struggling to see the funny side of life.

I thought I was still writing for doctors in training and took a while to realise that CME is for all doctors, junior and senior. I also became aware of the pitfalls in writing lighthearted pieces for a quarterly journal. In the months between deadline and publication, things happen and the public mood can change. But comments, negative or positive, were rare. The only real feedback was that successive editors kindly allowed the column to continue.

TOG was published online and on paper until the pandemic struck in 2019. A decision was then made to publish online only. I blogged on in cyberspace until 2023 when *TOG* was reorganised and finally "*And finally*" disappeared..

JOD

More education, anyone?

It is a heavy responsibility to write the first '*And finally*' page of this new journal. I have to think of two very different groups of readers. There are the right-handed ones who started at the front and are exhausted after filling in all those 'true/false' boxes, and then there are the left-handers like me, who crack open their journals at the back, eager for the educational delights that lie ahead – or rather, behind. The two groups may have differing views about continuing medical education.

Lip service

Education is supposed to be one of those things like evidence and empathy, of which no doctor can ever have too much. Indeed, it is at the top of the Government's wish-list: what Britain needs is a skilled and flexible workforce. The unemployed and the potentially unemployed must re-train to make themselves more marketable.

Re-training, though, is not education. As Sir Kenneth Calman, now top educator in the land of the Prince Bishops, says: 'To be trained is to have arrived, but to be educated is to embark on a lifelong journey'. Nonetheless it can be hard to tell the difference. I often think my most useful educational attainment was learning to type with all my fingers: on that journey I can go no further.

It is universally acknowledged that learning is a jolly good thing but when everyone agrees, someone should get suspicious. Do people really want better-educated doctors? Already we are the longest-trained people in the country, but the public seems increasingly unhappy about us thinking for ourselves. They want us to follow guidelines laid down by others. Those of us who don't may be given a hard time.

This is the vogue, despite the demonstrable incompetence of some medical protocols – notably, the notorious 1995 guidelines on pill prescribing, which came into force before Britain's skilled medical workforce had a chance to assess the evidence. They have at last been withdrawn after causing thousands of unplanned pregnancies.

View from the ivory tower

The professed enthusiasm for better educated doctors does not sit easily with the wish for a compliant profession doing as it is told by NICE or indeed by the Royal Colleges. Education has a track record of making people eccentric and ready to disagree with authority or with one another. You can tell I am a veteran of academic committees. Another insight from university life is that nowadays education dares not speak its name on campus. It has become 'teaching and learning'. Dissecting education into its component parts has not added to its vitality but has made it easier to measure. Teaching quality is assessed against set objectives.

I have always thought it arrogant for a teacher to set goals, particularly in postgraduate education. Even at undergraduate level, we professors would do well to remember that sometimes the learners are smarter or wiser than the teachers. If education really is a lifelong journey, as Sir Kenneth suggests, it involves teacher and pupil travelling together and learning from each other.

In an ideal world

The ideal medical education would begin not with three A-levels but with a broad-based Baccalaureate. Medical school would include a sprinkling of the liberal arts and a rediscovery of the essay. Postgraduate education must include technical skills and detailed knowledge –this is what people go to doctors for – but would not end there. CME points for an evening at the National Theatre? Why not – provided we can prove we stayed awake.

If we really were educated rather than trained, we might have more self-confidence as a profession. The letter pages of the weekly throwaways might contain less petulance and paranoia. We might become sufficiently urbane and literate to persuade other professions (even the law) how medicine should develop, and to listen to their views without being overawed.

By now, the right-handers must have nodded off. Go to it, left-handers: prepare for urbanity.

Clearing out the library

Our house is slowly filling up with books. A few are large and elegant but most are small, soft and functional. We cannot bring ourselves to throw the old ones out - although *The 1962 Guide to East Anglian Pubs* has come close once or twice. But how could we consign it to bonfire or wheelie bin? It would have to be buried respectfully in the garden, like the children's hamster.

There is of course a shelf of textbooks preserved since our student days. Should we ever feel the urge to check on Starling's law of the heart or the innervation of the lumbricals, we can reach for them, well thumbed and with those desperate underlinings from a pre-highlighter era. They represent ultimate authority.

Today's undergraduates retain this instinct despite the overhyped advantages of the world-wide web. In the outpatient clinic they furtively consult an Oxford *vade-mecum* to check on the consultant's pronouncements. Or in some cases, in preference to listening to the consultant at all. *Mea culpa*, I know I shall not mind *so* much when it is our textbook they are reading.

The book has a symbolic power that its successors will never achieve. To that extent it is like the sword. The statue of Justice on top of the Old Bailey would not command the same respect holding a Kalashnikov. Nor would a vicar carrying a laptop into the pulpit. Many fellow academics believe that tomorrow's Davidsons and Jeffcoates will achieve eminence by writing classic interactive CD-ROMS. 1 doubt it.

The departmental library

So I had mixed feelings when my laboratory-based colleagues suggested that we cull our departmental library. Nobody, they said, consults journals that are more than five years old, and as for all those books! I could see what they meant. Some of our teaching consists of student presentations and, as facilitator, I squirm when the youthful speaker has obviously based the talk on the largest, oldest (and most American) book available.

With space at a premium and no second-hand market, our pre-1990 journals were trundled away by the porters. Then in went our most ruthless specialist registrar. Soon we had enough empty shelves to last well into the new century and the books, apart from an up-to-date rump, were piled on the floor.

I asked for a few moments alone with them. Would anyone notice, I wondered, if I quietly replaced those written by my friends? Some, after all, were classics. And what if yesteryear's practice comes back into fashion? Under pressure to lower caesarean section rates we might rediscover *Browne's Antenatal Care* of 1960. 'Contracted Pelvis: Trial of labour ... is suitable for young primigravidae with a true conjugate of 3½ inches (8.9 cm) or more'.

Some of them were not out of date at all. *Medical Staffing Structure in the Hospital Service* (also from 1960) commented: 'Work properly belonging to consultant posts is regularly being discharged by ... members of more junior grades. The factors responsible ...include the financial restrictions to which hospital authorities are subject .... There is a noteworthy absence of testimony that the present structure has proved satisfactory. ...'

The rate of consultant expansion during the 1950s, I read, was 1% per year, and in 1958 over 60% of senior registrars in obstetrics and gynaecology were aged over 35 years.

Other books had dated but still gave a sense of history. *Male Disorders of Sex*, published in 1930, included a chapter on masturbation: 'Anaemia is frequently found ... and Veeki states that he has even seen a minor form of epilepsy ... that was entirely due to masturbation. By the application of an ingeniously arranged bandage which effectually prevented self-abuse, the attacks were cured.'

Eventually, the department staff persuaded me to come out. If you are thinking of helping, it is too late. The porters have done their duty.

On the waterfront

Dateline: Cape Town, 7th October 1999
The Table Bay Hotel is undeniably posh. One side faces Robben Island, small on the horizon but big in South African history. The other side overlooks Cape Town's waterfront, now billed as 'Africa's premier shopping mall' – and arguably the world's most scenic.

Today, there is no 'tablecloth' on the famous mountain and conditions look good for our evening flight home. Around the quayside are street entertainers and occasional groups of gynaecologists, pink in the spring sunshine, remarking to one another that on balance this is better than Thursday outpatient clinic.

It seems more than five days since we were standing in the airport arrivals hall, clutching our slides or posters and asking ourselves whether any medical gathering – even an RCOG international scientific meeting – could be worth all this hassle. Jumbo jets, like buses, tend to arrive in convoys and long queues at Immigration had left plenty of time for introspection.

In our Sunday best

The meeting had indeed been worth it. Success depends on a lot of planning and a little luck, and fate had toyed with the Council until just before Sunday's opening ceremony. At the eleventh hour, the intercontinental freight system had yielded up the new Fellows' gowns and the last of the Councillors' suitcases, and the College's first blue-jeans admission ceremony had been averted.

An immaculately dressed procession had mounted the steps of the Jamieson Hall at 6 p.m. local time, just as the Springboks were kicking off at Murrayfield in the rugby world cup. Betting persons take note: a pattern is developing. As in the 1998 soccer world cup, a British team playing during an RCOG congress opening ceremony narrowly lost.

Sunday started sombrely with a pre-congress discussion about violence against women. This was a topical subject. A debate was raging in the *Cape Times* about a television commercial in which an actress inveighed against South African men for their tendency to rape women. Some men had objected to being stereotyped and the commercial had been withdrawn. Cowardice, fumed the letter writers.

Science and art

For the next three days the meeting ran like clockwork. A congress in full swing is an awesome sight. Participants checked their slides, kept their talks to time, asked questions, chaired charmingly, stood by their posters and just occasionally picked up one another's bags in error. Computerised presentations, by and large, worked.

Each delegate would name different highlights but there are always some big hits that electrify everyone. Dr Eddie Mhlanga is a gynaecologist who works in the South African Department of Health. In the opening session on fertility regulation he followed two celebrated speakers by sitting beside an overhead projector on the huge stage and showing hand-written acetates. His talk was a brilliant combination of wisdom and legibility.

Some cultural lectures live in the memory, but usually only one per congress. This time we were inspired by Africa's cross-border Peace Parks and impressed by Stellenbosch's Botanic Garden. How could Charles Wright, of Hillingdon, Middlesex, follow those talks and how could he dare to lecture on African history? It turned out that Charles had long ago fallen in love with Africa and that he knows everything about the Anglo-Zulu war of 1879. He knew who Rorke was and what 'drift' meant, and he had pictures of the real people played by Stanley Baker and Michael Caine. Most importantly, he valued the art of storytelling. We were spellbound.

Another century, another waterfront

In her speech at the final banquet, the local chairwoman remarked that, just when she had learned how to run a congress, it was all over. Zephne van der Spuy said she was keen to do it all again but she won't have to. Speaking from somewhere inside a large Australian rugby jersey, Michael Chapman invited us all to Sydney in 2002. Bonzer, cobber.

The web page

Now that the nineteen-nineties have given way to the twenty-naughties, I have taken another step into the world-wide web. January saw me logging on to the Royal College of Obstetricians and Gynaecologists' website and registering for the first time to gain access to the Fellows' and Members' area. (Note the apostrophes. They show that I am not yet fully converted to web culture – true 'webbies' rarely use them, and never in the right places.) Like all converts I am overcome with zeal. I logged on in various places (all respectable) and now I have a fistful of passwords. They are not very imaginative. To join, say, a library, you type your name, postcode, mother's maiden name and father's size in socks into boxes on the screen, and later an unfamiliar envelope arrives through the post. Inside is a note which says 'Your username is DRIFE. Your password is LIBRARY'.

Flushed with excitement you return to the site. Your pulse races a little as you enter the forbidden zone. What do they get up to in here? Sure enough, the interactive area turns out to be a place where anything goes. Participants are free to say what they like, ignore the rules of grammar and even use exclamation marks.

Virtual authors

Webchat is more like a telephone conversation than a letter. E-mails have more in common with spoken communications than with written ones. Now that I realise this, I am beginning to understand why I disagree with all those people who predict the demise of hard copy. For over a decade now, enthusiasts have been saying that soon paper journals will cease to exist. Articles, they say, will be published on the web and read on personal computers or mobile phones (which might keep them quiet for a while).

What I have been wondering is – who would write for these virtual publications? How many authors would be willing to spend time researching a paper, thinking about it, drafting it, polishing it, responding to referees and editors and then correcting proofs, in order to have it posted into cyberspace?

One of the obscure attractions of contributing to medical journals is that, unlike newspapers; some are not thrown away. It is still possible to go into a library, open a Lancet or BMJ from the 19th century (admittedly, sometimes separating pages for the first time) and make contact with writers long dead. They would be pleased to know that they can still startle or amuse readers a century on.

Would they have taken the same care if their work were simply to be scrolled on screen? I suspect not. There is a big difference between a virtual page and the on-line version of a printed one. I am composing this piece on a screen because what I write can easily be changed, but once printed it will be fixed, for better or worse.

With a printed journal, I can see the reader in my mind's eye. I know that she or he is intelligent, perceptive, reflective, witty, good-looking, NS, GSOH. With the virtual reader, I am not so sure. Webbies are different from you and me.

59

Electronic archaeology

I worry that the electronic age will leave no history. Looking back. we respect the Romans and Egyptians because they built in stone and wrote on paper. Web authors will be like the Goths and Huns, who built in wood and had an oral tradition. Their culture has disappeared and we think of them as barbarians.

You may not believe me, with all the electronic hardware in our offices, but the process is already happening. In a drawer at home are reel-to-reel audio tapes of my grandfathers speaking – one a Scottish minister and the other a chapel deacon, reciting in Welsh. I know the recordings well but I have not heard them for 20 years because the machine on which they were made is defunct and obsolete.

They lie among tape cassettes containing articles I wrote on my first word processor (which is somewhere in the garage) and large floppy disks for my second, also now unreadable. No doubt in the future there will be university departments of electronic archaeology – dedicated to deciphering magnetic documents: but how much more convenient to have them on paper in the first place.

Hail Fellow, web met

For anyone uninterested in posterity, though, the built-in obsolescence of the web is attractive. Its conversations, like saloon-bar discussions, will soon be forgotten and one's sillier thoughts can always be blamed on hackers. If you have a view on this, post your comments on the College website. Someone claiming to be me might answer.

Remember the millennium?

This time last year, people were starting to get excited. Hospitals were employing staff to seek and destroy the 'millennium bug'. Doctors were discussing – and, to their credit, often rejecting – the idea of being paid a king's ransom for one night on call on 31 December. Managers were forming committees and cascading information.

The Royal College was receiving a steady stream of enquiries from journalists who seemed to believe that every British couple of reproductive age had gone to bed early on10 April with a bottle of plonk and an urge to try for the 'millennium baby'. The media were none too pleased to be answered by common sense and, as the calls kept coming, increasing exasperation. 'It's just a fun story, doc,' they protested. 'Don't take it so seriously.'

It all seems a long time ago now. Already my memories of the event itself are in black and white, like the coronation. 'What did you do in the millennium, Daddy?' Well: actually, I volunteered to be on call. Some time in the mid-1990s I had predicted a problem with the rota on the last Hogmanay of the century. When challenged about my own plans I had pompously said I would be at my post. Fate, in the form of a mischievous secretary, made sure that I was.

Late on Millennium Eve, I thought I should drop in on the labour ward. Not that I took the bug seriously, you understand. As I arrived, there were cries of disappointment – the only woman in labour delivered at 23.57. Not that we really wanted the millennium baby. It would have been too 'naff' for words. A bug-free midnight came and went and we stood at the window, drinking orange juice from plastic cups and watching distant fireworks. Not that we minded, you understand.

Hold the exhibition

The College was planning to hold a millennium open day and exhibition for spring 2000. Both were put on hold when the date was set for excavating the garden. The opening of the new education centre next year will be a better time to invite the public in and show them what the College does.

I feel impatient. Although the exhibition will look forward as well as back, I doubt if the future will equal the achievements of the 20th century in improving the health of British women. No matter how familiar I become with maternal mortality statistics, the 50-fold reduction between 1935 and 1985 still evokes a sense of wonder. But how to convey this in an exhibition? Parties of schoolchildren are not going to be amazed by a graph, and it might be a bit much to ask Madame Tussaud's to recreate a forceps delivery on a kitchen table.

It will be good to celebrate the high-tech achievements of Ian Donald, Patrick Steptoe and Robert Edwards; and of course there must be room for those who were not Fellows of the College, like pioneers of family planning and the inventors of the pill – but ultrasound, in vitro fertilisation and contraception are familiar facts of life to anyone under thirty. The young, as ever, are likely to be blasé.

A sense of history

Looking back over a millennium is all very well, but what really fascinates is change in one's own lifetime. This is why an interest in history, like a paunch, develops with age. For me, the most intriguing change is in attitudes. It is hard to believe, for example, that as recently as 1966 the British Medical Journal was inveighing against vasectomy. A leading article on 25 June stated that, compared with sterilisation of the female, 'the operation on the male . . . would seem to raise different ethical issues'. It concluded, 'its performance in a healthy man for a purpose other than the protection of his own health is difficult to reconcile with the traditions that normally guide clinical judgement'. The ideas may be quaint but the oracular prose is still impressive.

A good way to develop a sense of history is to browse among ancient correspondence columns. When you immerse yourself in a long-forgotten debate, it is by no means clear who is right. The arguments of the dinosaurs seem as cogent as those of the innovators until you raise your head and look through the retrospectoscope. It helps you to develop a healthy scepticism about today's controversies. Mind you, it is no help at all with a millennium exhibition.

The pedant's revolt

If you were thinking of emailing me, don't bother. I know that, come next December, pedants will be celebrating the true millennium: 2000 completed years since 01/01/01 AD. (I wonder how a pedant celebrates – perhaps with exactly 90 ml of champagne or a rocket fired at 85.4° to the patio decking.) So our celebrations in 2001 should keep everyone happy.

From the press officer

Even with its new professional public relations team, the College will still need Fellows and Members to talk to the media. Not all of them are keen on this. Some of our more articulate colleagues loathe the idea of live interviews. Others have been hurt by being misquoted and do not want to repeat the experience. Doctors who appear too often in the media do not always endear themselves to their colleagues. The media themselves look down on 'rent-a-quote' politicians and the same can apply to doctors. Yet the medical profession's image needs boosting, as a taxi driver pointed out to me at some length the other day.

Good relations

Public relations work can be divided into 'proactive' – approaching the media with your story – and 'reactive' – commenting on other people's. In practice there is overlap between the two. A story that you generated can ricochet around the media and rebound on you unexpectedly, weeks or months later. Conversely, a request for a comment on someone else's news can provide a good opportunity for putting across the College's point of view.

For example, recently the phone rang unexpectedly: a radio journalist was preparing a programme about consultant expansion in the NHS and wondered if the College had a view on this. Some time later, when I paused for breath, he suggested meeting over a tape recorder. It turned out that a colleague had primed him. When the programme was broadcast, it included a gratifying segment in which the journalist gave a government minister a hard time over the lack of obstetric posts.

When you work with the media you quickly lose any illusions that you, or anyone else, can control the news. You also realise that a single national news item – even on Radio Four or on a tabloid front page – will not change the world. What you need is persistence. The same story, told afresh each time to a different reporter or young programme researcher, may eventually shift public perception and influence the focus groups that drive the Government.

It is not always easy to sound fresh. News journalists work to a different daily rhythm from other people. Their peak times - 6 a.m. (for the morning radio) and 6 p.m. (for the next day's papers) - are not the hours of maximal alertness for most of us.

Hold the front page

Low-key persistence may be most effective but it is the high-profile dramas that cause the biggest upheavals, in Sussex Place as in the wider world. Sometimes the College can brace itself. We usually know when a government report or a GMC verdict is imminent but never exactly when the phones will start ringing. In general, it will be at the most awkward moment possible. The Government likes to release important policy documents when everyone is about to go on holiday, and the GMC's Professional Conduct Committee has been known to announce its findings at 6.30 p.m. on a Friday. All the news media want comment instantaneously, simultaneously, from a doctor, and in person. It is a mixed blessing that the College is midway between BBC television centre and ITN, with Broadcasting House just down the road. The real problems are ensuring that the media's minicab driver can find the College and avoiding tedious delays in getting past the commissionaires guarding the studios.

Big stories are not always bad news. When Leo Blair's birth was imminent we had the rare pleasure of telling the press that we could not possibly comment, except in very general terms. When the world was told that medical science could reverse the menopause we went into misinformation-correction mode and the media were so avid that they sent a radio car. Its telescopic satellite dish suddenly appeared, like ET, outside the second-floor window of the Fellows and Members' room.

Each interview is like applying Kielland's forceps: you are conscious throughout that something might go wrong and you don't stop worrying after the procedure is complete. But the College cannot sit behind closed gates and hope the press will go away. College spokespersons walk a tightrope: comment often has to be guarded but, in general, honesty is the best policy. Journalists can sniff insincerity and we can usually (but not always) recognise which journalists to trust. Colleagues who have allowed themselves to be persuaded to talk to the media have even enjoyed it. How do we audit our results? We shall know we are winning when a future cabby says, 'Obs and gobs, guv? Aah, lovely. Have this one on me.'

Professorial lecture

The worst lecture I ever heard was back in 1966. A nervous biochemist stood in front of us, scribbling formulae on the blackboard, rubbing them off again and talking to himself. One hundred and fifty medical students, bored at first, then bewildered, then angry, began barracking and leaving. Some stayed and reasoned with him. His next lecture was much better. Later he quite deliberately assumed some funny mannerisms and within a few years he was one of the school's celebrities.

I like to recall that story of redemption when I sneak a look at the feedback forms after College meetings. They are sometimes humbling but even when the general response is reassuring there always seem to be one or two people who grade your presentation as poor. You brood about them. What didn't they like? Was it the accent, the joke or the fact that you have not yet moved on to PowerPoint?

The lost art

A dozen years on from the biochemistry course, I was interviewed for a lecturer post myself. I have always wanted to lecture, I told the panel. But of course that is just what lecturers never do. Even in the seventies their main teaching role was to give seminars. Nowadays they facilitate self-directed learning. Universities do not like students getting together in large numbers. If a crowd starts to gather, a troop of educational theorists is sent in to break it up.

Students, though, like a good lecture. Its appeal is primeval – another thing I realised as an undergraduate. One of our social medicine teachers was a man of mature years with a red tie and a roguish expression. When he first strode into the lecture theatre the young woman sitting next to me caught the glint in his eye, put down her biro and leant forward, rapt.

Sex appeal does not feature in university appraisals, perhaps because higher education was an all-male business until Victorian times. Even then, however, charisma was valued. Some doctors made a good living by charging sixpence per student per lecture – a primitive but effective form of teaching quality assessment. Students attended, not because they could not read it up in books, but because of the thrill of a live performance.

Trial by fresher

All of which is by way of background to an invitation that arrived a year or so ago from the student organisers of our undergraduate introductory course. As Dean of Students, would I give a professorial lecture to the freshers? What do you want me to talk about? I asked. Nothing, they said: just give a professorial lecture. It is sometimes difficult to know when young people are sending you up.

Of course I accepted. I was honoured, though not as much as the nineteenth century deans whose talks were reproduced word for word in the *Lancet*. Around 1870 one of them argued that because of the explosion in medical science the burden of factual knowledge was now far too great, and students should concentrate instead on basic clinical skills. I toyed with the idea of simply reading it verbatim.

What the new students wanted to hear about, I decided, was the reality of being a doctor. That at least was something I knew. But the generation gap yawned between us. Telling them how it is for me now – the committees, the train journeys, the paperwork – would be crushingly boring. Telling them how it was for me thirty years ago would be – as my children would phrase it – sad.

Disrespect goes down well with a youthful audience but I suspected that incisive comments about my senior colleagues would probably be reported back to them. You can always tell stories against yourself but that might wear a bit thin after the first twenty minutes and, anyway, I wanted our specialty to retain some credibility.

In the end, I put together enough wisecracks about surgical registrars and media fantasies to fill most of the hour-long slot. Towards the end, rather to my surprise, my mood changed. Carried away by my own voice, I got serious, first about the global tragedy of maternal mortality and then about how proud I am to be an obstetrician. I wagged my finger at the two hundred faces. Lots of people, I said, will tell you they are fed up with medicine. Don't believe them. If they meant it, they would leave.

After the ball

There were no feedback forms, but about nine months later at a student ball a young man, emboldened by drink, started talking to me. 'I was thinking of giving up', he said several times. 'You were the only person in the first year who told us you were glad to be a doctor.' Of course, he was tipsy. You can't really believe him, can you?

Two-centre lives

The current crop of College Officers is now well into its third year of two-centre life. For each of us, the week is divided between London and our base hospitals, 60 to 500 miles away. These distances may not impress overseas readers. Britain is a small country compared with, say, Brazil or Kazakhstan. Nevertheless, anyone familiar with travel in 21st century England will be amazed at our tenacity.

Each of us has honed the art of personal transportation to near perfection. We know exactly the minimum time to get from Committee Room One to Coach H of our train. We have long since discovered that the Circle Line (of the London Underground) is London's equivalent of the Bermuda Triangle. We can tell you the best time of day for catching a southbound taxi at the back door of the College (11.15 p.m., since you ask, which is no help to us at all).

We do our reading on the train. Over the last two years, we have progressed from the briefcase to the pilot bag and then the wheelie luggage, as our files have grown and our vertebrae have shrunk. But we still need a bit of peace. That is hard to find, as technology advances and Cellnet reaches deeper into the tunnels out of King's Cross.

The Leeds train

The most irritating table companion is the stranger who takes out a mobile phone and sits looking at it, trying to think of someone to call, A close second are groups from the NHS Executive. This body has a large office in Leeds, so I often find myself unwillingly eavesdropping on discussions about primary care groups or postgraduate education. The discussants are much too cheerful and innocent to be doctors. They use the words 'overarching framework' without a hint of irony.

On one journey, a pair of NHS executives began with an ill-informed critique of the *Confidential Enquiry into Maternal Deaths* ('no normalisation of data') and progressed, after Peterborough, to a diatribe against obstetricians ('Sign whatever I want you to sign'). I sat opposite, making notes of what they were presumably telling Government ministers. The man was dismissive of care outside London. When the woman spoke

67

positively about her own labour he was incredulous: 'What, you wanted monitoring even though there is evidence that it doesn't do any good?'

The worst thing about incessant train travel is that it does not earn you Air Miles. Colleagues who regularly take the Heathrow Express (on which the phoners are marginally more interesting: 'Est-ce qu'il y a des messages pour moi, Chantelle?' 'Haben Sie fur mich einige Messages, Hildegarde?') are rewarded by gold or silver cards from the airlines and an aura of sophistication denied to earthly commuters.

The homecoming

Welcoming as the College is, the hospital still feels like home. Both have a group of smokers at the entrance: at the College they gather discreetly at a side door, but at the hospital they stand proudly with intravenous nutrition and nightdresses. Both institutions have teams of amiable receptionists but only at the hospital are the smiles and cheery waves protected by screens of reinforced glass.

Medical colleagues at home are wonderfully supportive when we phone to rearrange nights on call. Nurses and patients are surprisingly understanding as we appear on the ward at odd hours to keep up with patients who are being looked after perfectly well by the rest of the team. What is hard for us is the growing realisation that we are not indispensable. The hardest thing of all, though, is remembering the right password for the right computer. Email should have made life easier for itinerant Officers, but somehow our various systems don't get on with one another as well as they should. The big mistake on returning to the hospital office is to switch on the PC. That dramatic orchestral chord (which always takes me by surprise) is followed by a notice 'YOU HAVE 22 NEW MESSAGES', a brief struggle to resist and then a long session reading several days' accumulated trivia.

Why bother?

A management consultant, reading this, would ask why on earth we try to do two jobs. Surely College work is important enough to deserve full-timers? Surely the hospital managers want us there seven days a week? The answer is not just that the College could not afford it. The reason is more important than money, if such a concept can be imagined nowadays. The fatal weakness of those NHS executives on the train was that they have never worked with patients. Doctors who move on to non-clinical jobs quickly forget what it was like. As anyone with medico-legal experience knows, the confidence of an obstetric expert is directly proportional to the length of time since he retired from active practice. This is why we do it, I think.

The last of the doctor laddies

At our last MRCOG OSCE course in Leeds, I was next to one of the counselling stations. There, an actor played the part of a man with a short fuse, as candidates told him that his partner (as wives are called nowadays) was about to undergo a hysterectomy for postpartum haemorrhage. I tried to concentrate on my own station – an information leaflet on the menopause – but it seemed much less interesting than the raised voices behind the partition.

Other actors (as actresses are called nowadays) played the parts of clients (as patients ... oh, forget it) with tricky problems designed to test communication skills. During the lunch break we congratulated them on their credibility. They certainly looked and sounded like patients. The man had an ear stud and the women had just the right balance of diffidence and assertiveness. They modestly accepted our praise. Nobody pointed out that the candidates' acting skills had been almost as good. Stressed and knowing that these people were not real patients, they had come across convincingly as sympathetic doctors.

I, an actor

We doctors act more often than we care to admit. Most of us, however, have had little, if any, training. My own dramatic education started with school playlets, which burned themselves on to my memory through the intensity of my stage fright. Nevertheless, because my schoolmates had a healthy disdain for things thespian, I got the parts. Long before Sean Connery hit the big time I led the way in playing everyone, from Chinese peasant to Arab merchant, with an unreconstructed Scottish accent.

The climax of my schoolboy career came with a production of *The Merchant of Venice* to celebrate Shakespeare's 400th birthday. Rehearsals took place at a summer camp. A teacher with a cravat showed me how to bow with an Elizabethan flourish: 'Not so much of a throwing up gesture, dear boy'. In the sun-drenched Trossachs, our youthful stars succumbed to the charged atmosphere and paired up offstage as well as on, while we spear-carriers sublimated with late night parties.

The West Yorkshire Playhouse

For years I overcompensated by regarding actors as insubstantial luvvies. Yes, they can learn their lines and avoid bumping into the scenery. Yes, they can sing, dance, mime, project, modulate and empathise. Yes, they have the self-discipline to turn up punctually night after night and the nerve to go onstage even when everyone knows the play is awful. But what else can they do?

I developed more respect over a decade of visits to our local theatre, the West Yorkshire Playhouse. In the bar, the audience rubs shoulders with the cast, which, refreshingly, ignores the punters once its work is over. The actors look **so** young. My wife and I worry about them. When the play closes, will they work again? Some, however, are more senior. Last season's thrill was meeting Pip Hinton and telling her that I had fallen in love with her 45 years ago, when she appeared on black and white television in *Crackerjack!* She took it well and graciously allowed me to buy her a tonic water.

Visiting luminaries, such as Leslie Philips or Sir Iain McKellen, seem thoughtful professional men. Gone are the days of the 'actor laddie' –the pompous egotist with a loud voice and a limited range, who was tolerated because of his past reputation. Now, if an actor cannot deliver the goods, he or she is out.

Instant feedback

Actors and doctors share many characteristics. Both, for example, should be acute observers and both need insight into human nature. But where actors score over us is that they know what kind of impression they make. They do not need questionnaires, annual appraisal and five-yearly assessment. They are sensitive and their feedback is immediate, in the form of the silent telephone, the failed audition or the rustle of disapproval from the gallery.

Unlike actor laddies, doctor laddies can go for years sublimely unaware of what people think. If I bore my students, irritate the nurses or frighten the patients, they are too polite to tell me. Perhaps we should introduce curtain calls at the end of the ward round. This time, if I dried, everyone would be delighted.

Underground beauty

Until last month I could not have written this article. Any mention of the College's 'Dig Deep' appeal produced a pang of guilt. Then, in response to the President's final reminder, *I* sent off my banker's order and regained the moral high ground in a single bound. I may have missed out on having my name engraved on a seat in the new lecture theatre but, as some of us latecomers have pointed out to the Treasurer, there must be other seats (or perhaps lids) where our names could be immortalised.

Mother and baby

The College staff and office bearers have lived with the education centre for two noisy years. Its construction has provided the perfect excuse for standing and looking thoughtfully out of the window – an activity previously limited to us academics. Each stage has been fascinating in its own way. First, the JCBs appeared and promptly disappeared as they dug their way towards the Bakerloo line. We were apprehensive. What would they find – unmapped watermains, an unexploded bomb or, worst of all, Roman remains? Tight-lipped, we contemplated the prospect of all work stopping while we called in Tony Robinson and the Time Team.

We grew quite fond of the two digging machines. They looked like a mummy and a baby from Jurassic Park. The baby would dig out the corners and make a little pile which mummy would transfer upwards. With a single movement of her huge scoop, mummy would half-fill a lorry, and then she would daintily smooth the debris down so that no messy fragments fell on to Sussex Place as the tipper truck drove off.

Living on the edge

Soon our offices were perched on the edge of a cliff. We moved around gingerly, looking for the first warning cracks in the walls. The College Secretary tried to reassure us: "This is a listed building, not a listing building". Around the hole, a wall of metal was slid into place by eerily silent pile drivers. After that came the concrete, flat at first on the bottom and sides and then bewildering as pillars and walls appeared, seemingly at random. Like archaeologists in reverse, we tried to guess their future function.

In retrospect it is like a speeded-up film. One weekend a huge crane suddenly materialised. It stayed for the winter, wobbling slightly in the gale-force winds before vanishing just as rapidly. Looking up we could see, high in the cab, a man pulling levers to move distant objects with delicate precision. It was like minimal access surgery on a grand scale. But what most impressed us watchers at the windows was the logistics. Bricks, pipes: electrical equipment, glass, plaster and – mysteriously – enormous numbers of rubber mats appeared on time and in appropriate quantities as if by magic. Patrick, the unflappable ringmaster, should be put in charge of NHS waiting lists.

Finally, with the roof in place and the summer barbecue hours away, someone turned up with the lawn. It was unrolled during lunchtime. Craftsmen in hard hats crawled around putting the final touches to the stonework. We strolled on to the new terrace as the sun set and the concealed lighting came on. Perhaps it's the Pimm's, we thought, but by Jove you're beautiful.

Look, no thatch

Beauty was not a word that had sprang to mind during the mud-and-wellies stages. But now we came to think of it, aesthetic considerations had indeed been mentioned three years ago when Council, emboldened by rhetoric from its more visionary members, agreed that the project should go ahead. Now, when you go underground into the spacious atrium you feel a frisson that the architect must have intended all along.

Nowadays in Britain the adjective 'beautiful' is rarely used except by Brian Sewell or Bernard Matthews. In these cynical times it is hardly ever applied to women or buildings. To be admired by us British, a building must be two hundred years old or thatched – or preferably both. City dwellers are conditioned to do without visual pleasure unless they are excited by the logos of multinational burger chains. I blame the war. After the air raids, the only way we could live with the rebuilding was by pretending that elegance didn't matter.

Things are changing. Some of our ghastlier city centres are being redesigned and even our hospitals are beginning to think about their looks. Yes, I know that in most hospitals the only possible thing for an aesthete to do is curl up and die, but the newest ones give some hope for the future. Their doctors will want education in an inspiring environment and I think we've got one.

The cookery page

The English have a powerful appetite for cookery books. As I write, Jamie Oliver is all over the buses and Nigella Lawson's face is on billboards throughout London. Jamie is 'The Naked Chef' on television and Nigella is apparently his equal with the food processor as well as his superior with the word processor. But neither has produced a cookbook aimed at doctors – yet. Before someone else spots this gap in the publishing market, it is time for me to step in with my bid to become 'The Naked Gynaecologist'.

My culinary credentials

A spell on the RCOG Council teaches a chap self-sufficiency. Those early Saturday mornings in the kitchen of No. 8 Kent Terrace (the President's House) leave their mark. With all due modesty I may say that not many councillors have been invited to serve soft-boiled eggs to their colleagues – and have risen to the challenge, despite the risk of presidential sarcasm should they miss the 9.15am start. Here is my all-time favourite recipe for starting the day in a healthy but manly way.

Le breakfast 'Jim'

Ingredients

Orange juice	1 glassful
Cornflakes	0.6 bowlful
Milk	0.3 bowlful
Sugar	to taste
Toast (incinerated)	2 slices
Toast (underdone)	2 more slices

As a sophisticated, mobile, happening person you are expected to be able to make your own breakfast. In British hotels, unless you are determined to have kippers, a young person invites you to help yourself from the buffet and leaves you to it. Once you have discovered that under those bright lights the wooden handle of the scrambled egg ladle can reach 250°C, you think there is nothing else to learn.

The College provides stiffer tests. On a busy day in the President's House, half a dozen people, all just out of phase with one another, are preparing personal permutations of toast, muesli and bran while keeping one eye on the clock, not bumping into anyone and maintaining civilised conversation. It is like one of those displays of counter-marching at the Royal Tournament.

At the other extreme, try being the only person in the College at the weekend. In the silent corridors, can you find the corn flakes, milk, sugar (to taste) and a bowl? Then can you resist the urge to put them all together. It is oddly distressing to gaze at the sunshine breakfast and realise that you have no idea where the spoons are. (Concealed in a hidden drawer in the Fellows' and Members' Room. Remember who told you.)

But let's leave the College and go out into the big wide world of the NHS. Whether you are in a meeting, a clinic or theatre, lunch is simply a must. Or is it? Certainly everyone needs a lunch break – to relax, to go to the bank or to leave voicemail messages – but more and more people spend lunchtime telling one another that they never eat lunch. For them, here is the perfect mid-day recipe.

Nonlunch

Ingredients

Orange juice	that's OK – it doesn't count
Virtual sandwiches	imaginary tuna or absent avocado
Fruit	well, perhaps a grape or two

For trendy, tantric people like us, lunch is not so much a meal as a state of mind. Yoga, not yoghurt, so to speak. If you concentrate hard, one organic banana can raise your metabolism as much as steak pie and chips. And you will feel better. No more falling asleep at 3pm and missing the best bits of the meeting, the patient's history or the operation.

But even trendies need to pig out sometimes. After a busy day, what could be better than to get in touch with your roots, genealogically speaking. And what finer hinterland is there than Yorkshire.

A reet good supper

Ingredients

Fish	once
Chips	once
Mushy peas	twice
Newspaper	Yorkshire Post

The queue in a Leeds chippy is nothing if not cosmopolitan. Businessmen, urchins, newlyweds and men in baseball caps stand silently waiting while expressionless fish-fryers stare back. The secret of preparation is in the timing. If you get this wrong, you will find yourself behind a granny ordering for three families or a senior scout provisioning the whole troop. Just relax and read the small ads pinned to the wall. The wait will be worth it.

Mmm – delicious!

I think this is a jolly good start on the road to becoming medicine's answer to Delia Smith – don't you? Jamie and Nigella, eat your hearts out.

Farewell my Simpson

In January, Edinburgh's obstetricians held a rather splendid dinner in the Upper Library of the University's Old Quad. As an undergraduate in the 1960s I had spent much of my time in the New Quad (a mere 250 years old) and in what I now realise were lower libraries. The Upper Library turned out to be a high, beautiful room with books in alcoves guarded by marble busts of Caledonian high achievers.

I sat opposite Sir Walter Scott at a dining table long enough for over a hundred people – former SHOs, registrars and consultants of the Sirnpson Memorial Maternity Pavilion. Simpson himself had been brought out of his alcove and garlanded with what I suppose were the Scottish equivalent of laurel leaves; hardy leaves, perhaps. The occasion was to celebrate the closing of the hospital after 60 years and its move to a new site on the edge of the city.

The end of an era

It was a jolly affair, full of old acquaintance and hilarious reminiscence. A month later, however, it has already taken on an historic significance and a melancholy tinge. It is not just that 'February feeling'. It really was the end of an era.

The 20th century, for all its faults and occasional armageddons, was a good time to be a student of obstetrics. Did I really apply Kielland's forceps as an undergraduate? I can't be sure anymore but I do know I was confident with them four months into my first SHO post. Certainly I did perineal suturing as a student, although with a bedside manner – or bed-end manner – that makes me squirm at the memory. Those poor patients. But nobody complained. In the 1960s attitudes were based on a sense of social hierarchy that would astonish us now if we could remember it clearly. Most husbands had done military service and the army had trained them to respect officers. 'Salute the rank, not the man'. Medical students were perceived as officer cadets and treated with automatic deference.

Everyone knew the social code, so rules could safely be bent from time to time. At the dinner, a former hospital secretary – who went on to become Chief Executive of the NHS – recalled fondly how, in the 1970s, the registrar had helped him through his wife's labour by giving him a stiff gin from the doctors' mess. Ah, those were the days.

My anecdotage and proud of it

Tales from the last century may amuse the teller but they have a hypnotic effect – in the pharmacological sense – on the young. As children in the 1950s we found our parents' memories of war excruciatingly boring. Later, when we realised they were interesting, the stories had become formulaic through repetition. It is the same in hospital. When we greybeards begin reminiscing about life before the laparoscope and the photocopier, we can see the juniors on the edge of earshot sidling away to avoid making eye contact, while those trapped close to us glaze over and hope their bleeps will go off.

For sensitive fifty somethings, this induces a mild neurosis. We try not to mention the past. We feel apologetic for having gained extensive experience in the middle of the night as registrars. Although we are secretly proud of our skills we know that, according to current wisdom, our training was all wrong, so we don't like to talk about it in public. Which made that dinner all the more enjoyable. We could come out at last. Yes, we had enjoyed life in the mess, when we were the registrars in charge. For a short time the Simpson had been ours and we were sorry to see it go.

What's in a name?

The NHS, we were told, was considering dropping the name 'Simpson' after the hospital moved. Perhaps they had done a survey and found that the public thought it commemorated Homer. After all, rumour has it that this was why the Department of Health stopped calling itself 'DOH'.

We were outraged, of course. But now that the 20th century is becoming a distant country, is anyone still inspired by the 19th? Simpson's death in 1870 caused Diana-like grief and his funeral brought Edinburgh to a standstill. He was the classic Scottish hero – a baker's son from an obscure village, who went to university and became internationally famous.

Today his life story may fire up the annual Simpson Oration at the College but it leaves the general public cold. The only way to give him contemporary impact would be to make a movie about him, like 'Braveheart'. Come to think of it, Mel Gibson looks a bit like Simpson, and he can do the accent.

In the club

Most obstetricians and gynaecologists in the British Isles belong to a travelling club. It comes as a surprise to us to discover that consultants in other specialties don't. No wonder they look tense and depressed all the time. How can they survive without going off once or twice a year for a few days of relaxed 'shop talk'?

Local medical societies are not the same. By definition they are geographically static. Only the speakers move around and only lecturers with a touch of notoriety draw a large audience. Official specialty associations are different, too. They are very scientific, with bright young registrars giving papers and academics asking difficult questions; and they tend to meet in London, which is boring.

Travelling clubs, by contrast, gather in exotic locations like Swansea, Aberdeen or – everyone's favourite – Windermere. Members turn up in Barbours for spring and autumn meetings at home, and in bobble hats and luminous trousers for winter meetings abroad. I'm not a skier myself but I've seen the pictures. They are not a pretty sight.

Nogs and noggins

In the beginning there was only one club, the Gynaecological Visiting Society. It still exists. Its members never tire of telling the rest of us that they are older than the Royal College; which, indeed, sprang from their loins. It and other long-established clubs used to visit hospitals and watch members operate, an experience that by all accounts left the surgeon more scarred than the patient.

I started clubbing as a senior registrar in Bristol, where I automatically became a NOG. The Nuffield Obstetrical and Gynaecological Society (NOGS) filled the gap between London, which had the Victor Bonney Society, and North Britain, which had the Simpson Club. The patrons' names were symbolic. Gynaecological surgery held sway in the capital, obstetrics predominated in Scotland and in middle England we felt vague loyalty to Oxford.

Senior registrars' clubs liked to cultivate a bacchanalian image; for weeks before each meeting intending participants would 'talk up' their expected hangovers. As far as I know, however, hotel rooms remained untrashed and the batons of the Cumbrian Mounted Constabulary unbloodied. Yes, there were morning headaches but my happiest memory is of toddlers (NOGGETTES?) playing together in a hotel garden while their parents chatted. What made it sweeter was knowing that for once our consultants were on call without us.

Oldies but goodies

You had to leave after two years of being a consultant, so you simply formed a new club. Senior NOGS did not become SNOGS, alas, but called themselves the Nuffield Visiting Society. Ex-Simpsonians metamorphosed into the Northern Ireland, Northern England and Scotland society (NINES), so the next cohort called itself the TENS. Other clubs took ornithological names.

As members aged, the core business of science and socialising was joined by golf – a form of religion, I gather, which requires devotees to walk around outdoors in the rain in November. Among travelling clubs it provides stimulating challenges. For players: can I transport my clubs to the meeting, even on another continent? For the organiser: as a non-golfer, can I find a course?

Organising a meeting is a never-to-be-repeated experience, as demanding in its way as a biker's initiation rite. Despite postal services, telephones and email, an organiser only knows how many people are attending after the meeting is over, and sometimes not even then. He or she has to keep fellow consultants fed, watered and constantly amused, and on the coach has to respond cheerfully when they ask 'Are we nearly there yet?'.

There are compensations. One is the pleasure of finding out what your home town has to offer and what good research your colleagues can present in the morning sessions. Another is lasting gratitude. Long ago I glowed when a retired member whispered, 'Don't tell anyone, but this is the best meeting I've ever attended.' After he died we discovered he had said that, over the years, to each of us.

Clubs are good

In this egalitarian era, the word 'club' has unwanted undertones of exclusiveness. Travelling clubs worry about this and watch their gender and ethnic mix carefully, although each finds it hard to avoid an over-representation of Scotsmen. Nevertheless, those outside may feel suspicious and those inside may feel guilty. Such feelings should be dealt with firmly.

Clubs are good. They take you to places you might not otherwise see, and in a herd you travel with a light heart. Someone else worries about the group check-in and if anything upsets you, you can take it out on the organiser. You hear talks outside your subspecialty and you feel able to ask dumb questions, away from the gaze of your trainees. Above all, you meet colleagues who are still happy to be obstetricians and gynaecologists. Sometimes you have a good moan together but you always come back encouraged to carry on, at least until the next meeting.

Doctors' holidays

It's the time of year when we start dreaming of our next holiday. Our dreams change as we advance through our medical careers but we all agree that holidays are essential. Doctors and lay people believe that no human being can do the same job, week in week out, for more than six months without cracking up.

This is a modern delusion. Our forefathers and foremothers had to milk the cows, morning and evening, every day throughout the year. As a student doing a holiday job I remember the works forewoman remarking that she had never had a holiday in forty years. I was shocked. Was this physically possible? She had rings under her eyes but otherwise she looked fine.

The phrase 'holiday job' is a bit of a giveaway. If we really needed a complete break we would spend it in prayer, fasting and contemplation, which is presumably what was expected in the distant past, when the 'holy day' (notice, just one day) was the only break allowed from a life of constant agricultural toil.

'Holiday' now means different things to different people. For the likes of Thomas Cook it is a business opportunity. For the BMA negotiator it is paragraphs 874-923 of the new contract. For the working clinician it is something to look forward to with pleasurable anticipation and to look back on with nostalgia. The bit in between – actually going on holiday – is the tedious part.

Young, gifted and backpacking

Some holidays are special, though. Your first break from your first job is a wonderful feeling. Or rather, it was. Now that house officers – we're told – work more humane hours, they may not experience quite the same sense of release from bondage. In the bad old days we felt much like Edwardian mill workers must have felt at the start of the Blackpool fortnight. During our last day at work we were demob happy and when we left, the rush of joy was better than sex.

Nowadays it is different. The young doctor just disappears. The consultant naturally assumes this is another quirk of the new rota – a stint of night duty, perhaps, or a residential course on clinical governance organised by the human resources directorate. Then, two weeks later, the young doctor reappears, slightly tanned, wearing Inca earrings or carrying a shrunken head.

These days, the travellers' tales that hold the antenatal clinic spellbound come from the youngest doctors. Ah, the internet cafe in Tandjungredeb! And the ferry to Baclobalatu? Man, it's so crowded. It just keeps sinking. The trick is, watch the captain and when he jumps, you jump. You should eat plenty of garlic – sharks hate it. And put empty water bottles in your backpack for buoyancy, like they tell you in the hostel. It's really relaxing – we may go back.

The gite years

A thirst for adventure is a natural reaction to a supervised, regulated, protocol-driven job, but sooner or later most doctors reach the family holiday stage. This too has changed. Back in the days when I was the one wearing the waterwings, we went to the British seaside – returning every year, like salmon, to the same stretch of water. This unchanging ritual was our parents' reaction, I think, to participating in the Second World War. After years of not knowing where you would be from one month to the next, a settled routine was something exotic.

When we became parents, family holidays meant a French gite. Preferably close to the ferry port. ('Sommes-nous presque la yet?') In France everyday activities like shopping and eating were a mega adventure because, despite years of study the language remained deeply foreign. The public telephones were subtly and impenetrably different from ours and so we were incommunicado. Just paperbacks, vin ordinaire and le crazy golf. Wonderful.

Nowadays you call the specialist registrar on her mobile. 'Actually, I'm paragliding right now – can I call you back?' They never switch them off, you know.

Oldies on the move

Being an older consultant means, among other things, having more disposable income. But just because a holiday is more expensive, does that mean it is more enjoyable? You bet it does. It isn't just the money. Companies that cater for the senior holidaymaker know that the only way to keep a busload of Victor Meldrews quiet is through immaculate organisation and attention to detail.

For the academic, though, the urge begins to fade. You never get blasé about jetting off to conferences here and there as part of the job, and you are pleased that your accompanying person has developed an encyclopaedic knowledge of the world's art galleries. But somehow, your idea of a holiday is to disappear a few miles up the road to somewhere small and remote, with no mobile and not even any waterwings.

What not to wear

It is over a decade since I published any fashion advice for doctors. (Don't go looking for it - it was before search engines were invented.) In the interim we have seen many changes, including the feminisation of our specialty. This update is directed at doctors of the male persuasion. I would not dream of advising female doctors about anything, least of all clothes.

Except perhaps to point out the obvious – that the main sartorial aim of the female hospital doctor is to avoid being mistaken for a nurse, midwife or manager. A careworn but authoritative expression used to be enough but nowadays this is standard for all PAMs (professions allied to medicine). The young doctor should wear something expensive, to distinguish her from nurses and midwives, but should look as if she has put it on in a great hurry, to distinguish her from managers.

Men not in suits

The young male doctor owns a suit but wears it only when attending interviews or sponsored meetings well away from his hospital. On duty, his most noticeable fashion item is the stethoscope draped around his neck. My own stethoscope, bought in 1965 for a physiology course, consists of two black rubber tubes (getting a bit stiff by now) connecting the ageing bell to the frankly unhygienic earpieces. If I try to put it over my shoulders it springs off again.

Today's trainee, however, wears a designer stethoscope by Mr Littmann, the Versace of medical neckwear. The flexible plastic centre-section is usually colour coordinated with the doctor's socks. The stethoscope is not used for listening to things (there are small ultrasound machines for doing that) but as a badge of office, or just because it looks good – a kind of medical version of the pashmina.

Speaking of necks, whatever happened to the smartly knotted tie? Doctors under the age of thirty have developed a consensus that the tie should be worn loosely around the neck with the collar unbuttoned, like a St Trinian's schoolgirl. They think this indicates an independent spirit and an allegiance to evidence-based medicine. Others think it just looks scruffy.

The pyjama game

Theatre clothes used to be worn only in operating theatres. Now they appear all over the hospital, especially in the intensive care unit and the labour ward. Meanwhile, theatres allow people in outdoor clothes into their internal corridor. Eventually we shall reach the point where doctors wear ordinary clothes in theatre and blue pyjamas everywhere else.

Theatre pyjamas are comfortable but, like all clothes, we wear them for what they say rather than what they do. Theatre 'blues' tell the world that we are skilled technicians who have more important things to do than stop and talk. They set us apart from patients more effectively than a top hat and tailcoat in the old days. Wearing theatre pyjamas while taking consent from a patient will some day be challenged by a smart lawyer. And good luck to her.

Our next speaker

A lecture is a performance but, unlike other artistes, medical lecturers give little thought to costume. How to stand out from other speakers at that three-day meeting? A good talk helps but so does an eye-catching appearance, particularly now that all presentations use the same Powerpoint clip-art. A doctor has to be subtle. Not for us the flowing locks of Billy Connolly or the gladioli of Dame Edna. To make things even harder, only our upper body can be seen over the lectern.

Watch the seasoned lecturers. Lord Winston has made the moustache his own, Phil Hammond wears coloured spectacles and others have a range of bright bow ties. But be careful. Once you have chosen your logo, you have to stick with it.

Does my bank balance look big in this?

Sooner or later a consultant, unless he is a neonatal paediatrician, buys a Savile Row suit. He knows it will cost an arm and a leg but of course it costs twice that. Putting 'Savile Row' in front of 'suit' involves a spectacular mark-up, like putting the word 'medical' in front of 'equipment'. At those prices you think it will change your life, as in television makeover programmes where Cinderella, after trenchant advice, emerges from a changing room confident, witty and beautiful.

The tailors raise your expectations: "Oh, no sir, I only do the jacket. Our Mr Boggis is the trouser man." Deferential, they nevertheless radiate disapproval when they discover how much stuff – keys, wallet, mobile phone, College diary (remember them?), credit card holders and Swiss Army knife – you carry in your pockets. "Has sir considered carrying a handbag?" When sir finally emerges, confident and beautiful, he is disappointed to find that he does not stop traffic in Piccadilly. And, several months on, nobody in the clinic has noticed.

Good Europeans

The first time I left Britain was at the age of eleven on a school trip to Switzerland. The teachers, a husband and wife who represented between them the entire Maths, Science, Classics and Modern Languages departments of our village school, seem saints in retrospect but at the time they were terrifying Scottish authority figures. We kids spent all our time huddled together and didn't speak a word of Swiss the whole eight days we were there.

My next continental excursion was a grand tour after graduating MBChB. Four of us hired a small Renault at Calais and drove east. We had schoolboy French and a German phrase book, neither of which were much help behind the Iron Curtain. Eastern Europe seemed full of uniformed men with machine guns, not just at border checkpoints but randomly distributed along the road from Budapest to Zagreb. Even scarier were the nudists on the Yugoslav beaches.

The Babel thing

After such a xenophobic upbringing, did I over-compensate as a dad? Before our children were out of nappies we were in the queue for the ferry, the Maxi crammed with Pampers, heading for summer holidays in Brittany. Our toddlers seemed to enjoy the rustic furniture, Mammouth *supermarches* and parental Franglais but I don't think those annual jaunts hooked them on Europe. Grown up now, they prefer to go much further afield.

For me, cockfights in the Philippines or mountain sickness in the Andes have little appeal. Give me a pavement cafe and an incomprehensible local newspaper and I am a happy man. Anywhere between Paris and Paphos, or perhaps between Faro and Faroe – far enough to be foreign but near enough that if you're really stuck you can ask for the menu with the little Union Jack on it. Not that you ever would, of course.

Linguistic diversity is both a blessing and a curse. In the USA, doctors from, say, Boston and Charleston may make jokes about their cultural differences but they feel comfortable together and at least they can make jokes. For doctors from say Leeds and Lisbon, sharing an academic wisecrack is possible but cannot be done deadpan. It needs a fair bit of eyebrow work, certainly until you get to know each other.

Dites 'quatre-vingts dix-neuf'

As a doctor it isn't easy to be a good European. I feel much closer to specialist colleagues in Delhi than to those in Deauville (okay, okay – no more alliterations). When you go on a hospital accreditation visit to Bombay or Cairo you all speak the same language, literally and metaphorically. Amid the exotic sights you are struck by the similarities

85

with the UK – the BJOG in the library, for example, and the doctors who trained in London or Glasgow.

Touring a hospital in central Europe, by contrast, you are struck by the differences with Britain – the tiled delivery rooms, the enthusiasm for stirrups, the cleanliness... and the medical education. Medical students, we were told on one visit, spend most of their time attending lectures and have one week of exposure to clinical obstetrics. "But we think a week is not long enough" smiled our host as we registered polite shock. "So in future it will be two".

At conferences in Europe it comes as a surprise to realise that there are many doctors who do not speak English. Our image of the Euro-professional is of an urbane individual who talks our language with a rather attractive accent. We tell ourselves comfortably that there is no need for us to try to reciprocate because we would be so bad at it. We did get an O-level once but.. . . We assume that the speakers who rely on simultaneous translation are unsophisticated people with nothing important to say.

Mein lieber Herr Editor

In spite of all this, the *European Journal of Obstetrics and Gynecology* (the American spelling is significant) has had a British Editor-in-Chief in recent years. Now that Jim Thornton has moved to the BJOG (the abbreviation is significant), two professors have crowded into his vacant chair, my co-editor being Wolfgang Kunzel of Giessen. Germany.

Naturally all communications are in English. Italian referees write to the Italian Receiving Editor in English and in the publishers' canteen in Amsterdam secretaries chat in English. Yes, it is English, Jim, but not as we know it. As you read Euromanuscripts you find constructions that are quite understandable but obviously French or German or, for all I know, typically Polish. Trying to change them into standard British medicalese leaves you feeling clumsy and pedantic. Better not to bother, I think, and to save editorial energy for correcting the English of authors from England. Once you get used to it, Euranglais is fun – written English with a rather attractive accent.

Creatures of the night

It is 11:45 pm and I'm settling down to some nocturnal word-processing. Should I be telling you this? Being an owl is not something one normally admits to in public. The moral high ground belongs to the larks – the people who jog at dawn, drive to work before rush-hour, do a pre-breakfast ward round and then spend the rest of the day feeling smug and yawning. I do try to be a lark. I can get to the hospital before my secretary and usually before those colleagues who still have to do the school run. In the corridor I croak a cheery 'Good morning!' but nobody is fooled, and if confirmation were needed I have now been outed by email. With messages timed automatically, the world can monitor an emailer's biorhythms. My outbox is most active around midnight. People have begun to notice, so I might as well own up.

There are plenty of role models for those of us who think we do our best work after dark. When I was studying for Membership (after the family had gone to bed, of course) my edition of *Bonney's Gynaecological Surgery* had on its title page a verse about "great men". . . 'tolling upwards in the night'. Longfellow, who wrote it, was probably an owl and presumably Victor Bonney was as well.

The evidence base

I believe owlishness is our natural state. Evidence from evolution suggests that our cave-person ancestors were at least partly nocturnal. Their menstrual cycle ended up in sync with the 28-day lunar month, so they must have spent much time in the moonlight. And they must have done a lot of stargazing, since birth signs are so universal. Indeed they became skilled astronomers, otherwise the zodiac would consist of constellations I can recognise, like the Plough, Orion and, er. . .

Most compelling of all is the evidence of the labour ward. Left to themselves, babies prefer to arrive at night. As an SHO in a large Scottish hospital I audited the timing of women's admission in spontaneous labour. The peak, I recall, was around 3 am and the nadir was twelve hours later. We juniors fell into step with this primordial rhythm and now I can't seem to get it out of my head.

When humans became hunter-gatherers they had to retire early and rise at dawn. Although we now hunt and gather at Tesco we still follow this pattern and teach it to our newborns. As teenagers they rebel, however, and for a while nature reasserts itself. They go out clubbing when the parents are ready for bed and they return just before we go to work. Over breakfast, Dad recognises the emotion he is feeling. It is called envy.

Halcyon nights

Until recently, trainee obstetricians had the opportunity to savour day and night consecutively, sometimes several times running. I preferred the night. Hospitals, like motorways, are more relaxed after dark. The day has endless distractions but the night is less frenetic. You even got the chance to chat to patients, who sometimes responded by telling you what was really worrying them.

Of course, it was only the doctors who burned the candle at both ends. Other night staff slept by day – sort of. They had chosen this way of life for reasons you did not enquire about, and were characterised by unflappability. They saw things in perspective. They knew who was going to need a section at 2 am, and you filled in the time by dictating discharge letters until they called you. To this day, I feel it is misusing time to get the Dictaphone out in daylight.

The SNOG diploma

However rosy the view down the retrospectoscope, there's no denying that even owls got sleepy towards dawn. Intrapartum disasters used to occur around 5 am, and still do. To try to combat this, consultants in some places are now living in at night. We'll all be doing it eventually, although unlike yesteryear the night shift of the future will bring extra money, time off to recover and, no doubt, post-traumatic counselling.

I'm looking forward to it. Once again I shall be able to wear my College bow tie with pride, with its little symbolic shields – light blue for day, dark blue for night, and of course a star. I expect someone with no feeling for heraldry will suggest splitting into two colleges, the RCDOG for day people and the RCNOG for owls, but I don't see that happening.

We could have a specialist association, though – the Society for Nocturnal Obstetricians and Gynaecologists, with its own tough entrance exam. Part One will have MCQs about Big Brother and UK Gold. The Part Two SNOG could have OSCE stations on getting food from faulty dispensing machines, finding case notes in a deserted records department, or taking a call from someone in a disco who thinks her membranes may have ruptured. Only owls need apply.

Mr Growser

Brace yourselves while I reminisce for a moment. Back in the 1950s, *Children's Hour* on BBC radio had a series called *'Toytown'*, starring Larry the Lamb and Dennis the Dachshund. The supporting cast included Ernest the Policeman and Mr Growser (his name rhymed with 'Scouser'). Mr Growser was a crusty man in what sounded like late middle-age, and he complained about everything. His catchphrase was: 'It's disgraceful. That's what it is. Disgraceful!'

Fast-forward fifty years. Larry and Dennis have passed into radio history and dim-witted coppers have had an image makeover. But the spirit of Mr Growser lives on. His mantle descended briefly on to television's Victor Meldrew but now it has passed to me. I have become Mr Growser.

Complaining or grousing?

Grousing is narrowly defined. A grouse is something more than a grumble but less than a complaint. Grumbling can be good-humoured and vague – for example, we grumble about the weather but we know that nothing can be done about it. Complaining, by comparison, is focused and much more serious. We British hardly ever do it but when we feel driven to complain it is over some major injustice, like a strange car parked in the consultant's space.

Between these extremes lies Mr Growser territory. What winds him (and me) up are those minor annoyances of life that you can tolerate for the first – say – fifty-six years but which eventually get to you. The National Health Service is rich with examples but of course you find them everywhere else as well. For instance…

Queuing in post offices ('It's disgraceful.Why don't they have a special counter for those of us who simply want to post things?'). Being frisked at airports ('Do I look like an international terrorist, sir? It's disgraceful!').

Travelling by train ('What do you mean, there's no restaurant car today? It's … Words fail me.'). Or going to the theatre ('Look here, my man, you have been selling *The Big Issue* on this spot for seven years now. I take it you are sponsoring tonight's production?').

Mentioning post offices reminds me … Once, spending longer than usual in a post office queue, I took out my mobile, checked with Directory Enquiries and called the other side of the counter. I watched as the supervisor, idly chatting, went to answer his phone and I still enjoy the memory of his startled face as he realised where the call was coming from. This qualifies as a grouse, not a complaint, because it achieved nothing. He simply retreated into his office and shut the door.

Mr Growser FRCOG

But it is the hospital that gives us grousers endless opportunities. We start at the front door ('Disgraceful! It says No Smoking, Sir. And watch that cigarette; your nasogastric tube is melting.'). We wait for the lift ('Out of order every second month since 1991.   Disgraceful!). We go to the clinic ('For heaven's sake! This patient has completely run out of sticky labels. That does it! I'm taking early retirement.').

Over coffee and a soothing custard cream, we explain the theoretical basis for our grousing. You see, the reason that there are so many irritations in hospitals nowadays is that the staff are divided into those who do the work and those who are in a meeting. What is missing is a group in the middle – people who know what our little problems are and who can do something about them. A prosperous nation, we point out, is one with a large middle class. The strongest army is the one which has the best non-commissioned officers. But in today's NHS there is nobody between those who cascade the bullet points and those who see the patients. Anyone on the shop floor who shows any initiative is taken away, put in her own office and given a schedule of meetings to attend. It's disgraceful, that's what it is.

Avoid apoplexy

The secret of enjoyable grousing is to take it steady. You do not want to slide into passive acceptance but nor do you want to feel too strongly. It can happen. Irritating events occurring in quick succession can lead to apoplexy. This is hugely entertaining for bystanders, provided it is being directed at some distant target, but it makes you inarticulate. You may succeed in getting the chief executive out of the board meeting but you cannot tell him or her why.

Apoplexy worked for me only once, long ago when I was a registrar. Having taken a patient with a suspected ectopic pregnancy to theatre in the middle of the night I found there were no trousers in the changing room. I phoned the laundry manager at home and explained why I was pacing around in my underpants and about to operate in a dress. There was nothing he could do right now, he said, but next day an articulated lorry arrived with more theatre blues than we knew what to do with. This was not a happy ending. Shortly afterwards, managers everywhere went ex-directory.

Understanding the British

The Membership Admission Ceremony is one of the best things about being on the College Council. I have other opportunities to dress up in a gown and watch diplomas being handed out but the day at the College is special. Unlike university examinations, only a minority of candidates pass the MRCOG examination and most are from overseas. As we councillors look out at these talented people, we sometimes wonder what they think of us.

After the ceremony we mingle and chat with new Members and their relatives. Sometimes someone says they recognise me from this page. I wait, hoping they will add that I am far better looking in the flesh, but generally they change the subject. Recently one was frank enough to add that she hadn't understood these articles until she came to work in the UK. So, for *TOG* readers far from Regent's Park, let me try to make amends with a brief guide to the British.

Who are the British?

Geographically Britain includes England, Scotland and Wales, so we're a mixed bunch. Northern Ireland is part of the United Kingdom (a name used only by officials and statisticians) but half the people who live there really want to be British. The Scottish and Welsh are completely different:

half of them don't want to be British. People in England, always blissfully unaware of other nations' feelings, assume that 'British' means 'English'. The Celtic nations still resent the English for conquering them, centuries ago. The English don't notice and save their resentment for Europe. They detest the French and Germans, or at least they say they do. This is because, deep down, the English are French and German. In 1066 in southern England, the Saxons (Saxony is part of Germany) were defeated by the Normans (from France). Neither side has yet come to terms with this.

The Normans formed the English upper class and even today in Britain a French-sounding surname has a certain cachet (perhaps I should change my name to 'James de Rife'). But as anyone familiar with English sports fans knows, the Saxon proletariat are stubbornly resisting 'frenchification'. They still like to drink beer, eat sausages, put on weight and listen to brass bands.

Of course, it's not that simple. England is divided into halves, north and south, and until 1066 the north was full of Danes. Danish settlements had names ending in '-by', so today we have towns called Whitby, Wetherby, Grimsby, etc. The Danish colonists got as far south as Rugby. Most of those celebrating England's recent world cup success knew that rugby (the game as opposed to the place) was invented by the upper class (i.e. the French) at a public school but few knew that it owes its name to the Danes.

The British as patients

People who migrate to an island tend to be independent-minded. Look at Australians or New Zealanders. Like them, the British don't like being told what to do. In the past, patients here seemed docile and obedient but they were just being polite. They generally ignored medical advice. Recently they have started arguing with the doctor, which at least shows they are now taking us seriously. Overseas candidates in the MRCOG tend to be taken aback when the OSCE tests their ability to calm down a short-tempered Saxon.

What the MRCOG does not test, thank goodness, is accent recognition. The British are not particularly musical but they have perfect pitch when it comes to social class. These days a posh accent is undesirable, except if you come from overseas. Among the English, regional accents are all the rage and the upper classes now try to sound as if they come from suburbia. This is why our Prime Minister has such an odd, non-BBC accent. The Chancellor of the Exchequer, however, and the Leader of the Opposition (who are Scottish and Welsh respectively) can still sound their "t's" without losing credibility.

The British as doctors

There are some very fine British doctors but their numbers are falling. British people don't like to touch one another or talk about feelings, so they are happy to leave the profession of medicine to other people. The typical British doctor of today is unlikely to be of either Norman or Saxon descent and is increasingly likely to be female.

Doctors are expected to embody the best national characteristics. The British expect their doctors to be fair minded, tolerant and good-humoured (this is how we British see ourselves. Don't laugh.). So when you attend the Membership ceremony, you will understand why most of the councillors (apart from the Irish ones, who really do have a sense of humour) have such a strange look on their faces. We're trying to be British.

Dancing with SPROGs

Back in the 1950s, long before I knew how to spell 'ceilidh', we spent our evenings listening to the radio. There was only the BBC, of course. It gave us Children's Hour at 5pm on the Home Service and comedy at 7.30pm on the Light Programme. Between these highlights came the boring bits – news, The Archers and for us listeners in Scotland, country dance music. Was Scottish dance music really broadcast every night? And did it always involve an accordion? It felt that way. As a boy I could not imagine how anyone would willingly listen to a whole half-hour of strathspeys, jigs and reels with titles like "The 3rd Armoured Tank Brigade's Farewell to Munchen Gladbach" or "The Hens March o'er the Midden". Scots children in the 1950s were respectful but if I had had today's range of pithy phrases I would have suggested that the BBC should get a life or eat my shorts. Looking back, I see that I was receiving cultural imprinting. Not for us, today's daily dose of *Neighbours* and the ambition to call our firstborn Kylie or Jason. Instead, we were being subliminally influenced to name our sons after Jimmy Shand, the iconic accordionist, and to dance in the old Scottish way.

Body and mind

Now, in the 21st century, the folk-dancing gene is expressing itself more strongly than ever north of the border. I don't think radio is responsible and I'm not sure if dance still figures on target-driven educational curricula. At my primary school we were taught the basic steps and those of us with uncoordinated feet (dyspodia?) were kept at it until we got it right. It was worth the humiliation and fallen arches. Today I approach the Gay Gordons with a confident smile.

Our gym teacher, an aggressive man, shouted down any boys who complained that dancing was cissy. As the first pimples of puberty appeared, we realised he was right. Ours was a mixed school and Scottish dancing allows adolescent boys and girls to sublimate their burgeoning urges by hurling each other around the gymnasium in a stylised Celtic courtship ritual that melds music, sweat and Taekwondo in sublime physicality.

It also requires high-order mathematical skills. Scottish choreography is not syncopated but you sometimes have to count up to 32 or even 64. It also demands precise spatial awareness as you and your partner trace figures-of-eight, squares and diagonals, hoping to end up on the spot from which you started. A love of trigonometry underpins much Scottish culture, from engineering to Fair Isle knitting, and manifests itself on the dance floor too.

All of this should mean that Scottish dancing is a minority pursuit, like Morris dancing or plane-spotting. Not so. Everyone joins in, whatever their age or social status. The band does not need to target the punters by 20th century decade ('30s foxtrot, '40s quickstep, '50s jive, '60s twist, '70s pogo stick, '80s falling over, etc). All generations take to the floor together and expertise is unrelated to age. Participants are expected to start and finish at roughly the same time but the intervening near-chaos is what makes it a bonding experience.

Today's ceilidh band, incidentally, is unlikely to feature either accordions or bagpipes. An eclectic mix of instruments gives it an air of authenticity

94

and the bandleader patiently coaches the dancers through their moves. So this summer, when you see the word 'ceilidh' (pronounced kay-lee) on the social programme of your congress at one of Scotland's gleaming new conference centres, don't be scared.

Combating dehydration

All of which is by way of explaining why earlier this year I was seen with bow tie slightly askew after midnight in the bar of a country club near Edinburgh. The Scottish SpRogs, as they cheerfully call themselves, had crowned their educational meeting with a ceilidh, and the gender ratio (just right for the Dashing White Sergeant) meant men were at a premium. Overseas graduates quickly became honorary Scots and those of us of mature years discovered energy reserves we thought no longer existed. Unaccustomed exercise demands rehydration. As I clung to a restorative pint, SpRogs told me that Scottish babies have long since moved on from such old-fashioned names as Kylie and Jason. In Glasgow, apparently, there are now children of both sexes with the first name Pocahontas. And one, they said, called Versace McLatchie.

I believed them. Over drinks at one a.m., people tell the truth. This was why I came away both inspired and depressed. It was inspiring to hear how the SpRogs love their jobs and find our specialty thoroughly satisfying. But it was depressing to hear how their seniors were discouraging them. Consultants nowadays, it seems, are trying hard to talk young doctors out of a career in obstetrics and gynaecology. Shame on you. You should be dancing.

To Russia with love

The first time I passed through the Iron Curtain was in 1971. (Have I told you this before? It's easy to repeat one's Cold War stories.) Four of us new doctors hired a car in Calais and drove eastwards, more or less, to the Austro-Hungarian border. Our passports disappeared into a large red-brick building, an armed soldier searched our Renault 4 and eventually, for a large fee, we received 48-hour visas. I don't remember much about our short visit to Budapest but the submachine guns made a big impression. The phrase 'Iron Curtain' dates me. Nowadays, Budapest and Prague are relaxed easyJet destinations (only £27 from Luton) and Tallin and Riga are trendy venues for stag parties. But those of us aged over fifty years have had our perceptions shaped by a lifetime of propaganda. To us, everywhere east of the Elbe is grey and shadowy. A light rain is always falling, men in trilbies are watching your every move and a stone-faced woman is hiding in your hotel room, ready to kick you in the shin with a poisoned boot. Ian Fleming and John le Carré have a lot to answer for.

The Russian spring

Earlier this year we visited Russia with a group of itinerant gynaecologists. Amazingly, it was in colour, not black and white, and that was only the first surprise. The sun shone. In St Petersburg, Coca-Cola had sponsored some of the street signs. In hotels the muzak was by Andrew Lloyd Webber. In Moscow there were river cruises, spacious parks, eight-lane highways and traffic jams. The ATM machines asked if you wanted dollars, roubles or euros.

Everywhere, palaces had been restored at lavish expense. Our guide, Olga, seemed to be a royalist. Her voice shook with emotion as she described the murder of Nicholas II and his family. She was not alone in her sense of history. Leningrad's citizens had defended their city with their lives in the Second World War but they still voted to change its name back to St Petersburg in 1991. I think this makes a difference to how visitors feel about the place. We could try the same thing in the UK. Our Stalinist NHS should petition the Queen for a charter. The 'Royal National Health Service' – people would love it.

We were soon ambushed by Russian emotion. When the monks tolled the massive bell in their country monastery, the earth moved. Inside a dark church, the slanting sunlight, the icons and the priest's chanting put even hardened sceptics into a trance. Emerging from the ballet at the Bolshoi Theatre, unreconstructed chauvinists among us dabbed their eyes at the sheer beauty of the experience.

Hospital visiting

Not all Russian doctors speak English. Why bother, in a country with 145 million people and an empire stretching from the Baltic to the Pacific?

Giving a PowerPoint presentation through an interpreter is enjoyable, I found, once you settle into the rhythm. You have time to think of your next sentence and the English speakers in your audience enjoy being spared your usual verbal diarrhoea. You can also follow the local talks, almost, once you work out how to read the word 'gestosis' in Cyrillic.

Russian hospitals are passionate about preventing infection. For visitors, this means wearing overshoes or gowns but it also means the rooms are clean. Walking along corridors uncluttered by litter or bin-loads of dirty laundry, you know you are in a foreign country even before you reach the marble-lined delivery rooms. There, it seems, women deliver in twos, on tables side-by-side, with their feet in stirrups.

As smiling doctors show you around, you try to break through the awkwardness of language, culture and group behaviour. One of our hosts was pushing his colleagues towards evidence-based medicine. Another explained that their shiny new hospital had a well-connected medical director. A third welcomed us to a national referral centre for infection in pregnancy, with remarkably healthy-looking mothers and babies. Somewhere, a young doctor murmured that any patient wanting to see the professor has to bring cash in a brown envelope. Some of us began asking for details.

We meet again, Mr Bond

Back home, I rush to get the holiday snaps developed. They fix the memories. But what's this? No photos of the monastery? One 35-mm cassette must have got lost. More in hope than in expectation I phone the last hotel. (Did I tell you that the code for Russia is 007?) Yes, the chambermaid has found the film and handed it in. No, they cannot post it. Impossible. I will have to collect it. Or authorise an agent to bring it back to England.

So that's my story, M. One roll of film, locked away in Moscow, guarded by shifts of housekeepers 24-hours-a-day, with a few pictures of the tomb of Boris Gudonov and a very large bell tower. Any chance of sending George Smiley or Harry Palmer or even Miss Moneypenny? They must be desperate for something to do.

The problem page

The trouble with medical journals is that they rarely tell you what you really need to know. They may explain how to counsel a carrier of 3'-5'-rhubarbphosphorylase deficiency in pregnancy or how to perform laparoscopic omentectomy but they ignore trainees' everyday problems. So we are piloting a problem page where an anonymous expert, known only as The Prof, puts his 30-year experience of O&G at your disposal.

Dear Prof,

I am having trouble deciding which ringtone to choose for my mobile. What do you recommend? *Dr BT Orange*

Dear Dr Orange,

No doubt you have already checked www.cochrane.org and discovered the lack of grade A evidence on this question. Luckily I can supply grade C evidence aplenty. You should avoid gangsta rap as this will alarm your senior colleagues. Avoid 'Scotland the Brave' as this will annoy everyone else. Most tunes, even Lord Lloyd Webber's, eventually get on your nerves. I prefer a ringtone that sounds like a phone ringing but this makes everyone in the audience reach for their pockets or handbags when yours goes off during a lecture. Your College tutor should appoint a ringtone coordinator who will allocate a different tone to each trainee and ensure that no-one has the anthem of a football club they don't support.

Dear Prof,

What is the correct etiquette on the ward when you have to interrupt a patient watching a soap opera on her personal wall-mounted television? *Anxious Locum*

Dear Anxious Locum,

The GMC is keen to ensure that patients' autonomy is respected so you are wise to seek guidance on this difficult issue. Ideally you should adopt a multidisciplinary approach by consulting the patient's named nurse. She, however, will be on her break. You must knock before entering a patient's personal space but as you cannot knock on curtains you should carry a mallet and a small wooden board on ward rounds. If the patient is wearing headphones you should also carry a microphone and a portable loudspeaker to amplify the knocks. Some SHOs prefer a small siren. If she still fails to respond, put your request on paper and have it delivered by a porter.

Dear Prof,

Sister says my umbilical jewellery is too ostentatious. Is she within her rights to insist that I cover my midriff in outpatients? *Indignant LAT*

Dear Indignant LAT,

It depends on the midriff. Some can brighten up the clinic for an ageing consultant. Remember that Sister may be jealous, and be tactful. I notice that the Editor has shortened your letter for publication. In the original version you explain that the jewellery was inserted during your stag party while you were semi comatose. Ask your wife's advice, and consider suing the other members of your rugby club.

Dear Prof,

My consultant tells the same stories every week. I have heard them a dozen times and it is doing my head in. Should I whistleblow on him?
Trust Doctor

Dear Trust Doctor,

From your use of the phases 'doing my head in' and 'whistleblow' I suspect that you have recently arrived from Europe and are learning English from patients and free hospital newspapers in the doctors' mess. In British hospitals it is traditional for each consultant to have a limited number of reminiscences, which he recounts on a regular basis. The time to 'seek advice from a senior colleague' (not 'whistleblow') is when he stops. This can be a sign of clinical depression. 'Clinical depression' is common in the NHS: it is when the doctor is more depressed than the patient.

Hi Prof,

Your advice is really helpful. Do you answer questions by e-mail? Cheers. *SpR7@benbeculateachinghospitals.nhs*

Dear SpR7,

I never reply to any communication that begins with 'Hi' and ends with 'Cheers'. This saves me a lot of time when dealing with my inbox. I have not had to communicate with a hospital manager for years.

Dear Prof,

This morning in the doctors' car park I found my consultant had chained his bicycle to my door handle. What should I do? *Morgan Driver*

Dear Morgan Driver,

Do not assume that he is trying for a romantic attachment. He may not realise the Morgan is yours. He may have found his usual railing inaccessible or he may have arrived in the rain and thoughtlessly used the anchor point nearest the clinic door. Or he may have been trying to guarantee an audience of at least one for his afternoon teaching. I suggest you keep a pair of bolt cutters in the boot or trade in your flash car for a hatchback.

Dear Prof,

How do you get an anaesthetist to do an evac at the weekend? *Frustrated SHO*

Dear Frustrated SHO,

After thirty years in gynaecology I don't have the answer to this one. If anyone does, please get in touch. I have a patient waiting.

Prof on art

One of the things I had to give up for the sake of a medical career was the art class. Our school's curriculum for brainy kids was limited to academic subjects, which in those days included Latin and history as well as science. I don't feel I benefited much from my years with Virgil and Catherine the Great (or indeed from all that physics and chemistry) and I do resent my premature separation from art.

It meant missing some essential stages of post-adolescent development. My art student friends painted away their undergraduate years with dark meaningful pictures expressing serious angst. While they brooded, I doodled. If our talk turned to art they would smile pityingly at my taste in pictures and this led to a deep feeling of insecurity. I don't know much about art but I know what I ought not to like. If my gaze lingers too fondly over, say, a Jack Vettriano print I find myself looking around furtively. Are my friends watching?

But I still hanker after a palette and easel. There are a few gynaecologists who are artists and very good they are too, but my own participation is limited to watching Rolf Harris on BBC1 and envying his uninhibited enthusiasm. Perhaps when I retire I could become a wild-eyed abstract painter, drinking whisky from the bottle, bicycling around a large canvas, tossing pigments and yelling, "Can you see what it is yet?"

Rembrandt in Hampstead

For the time being, I content myself with dignified strolls round art galleries. They are strange places. Most artists intended to embellish the home of a patron or perhaps provide a focal point in a church. In a gallery their work is removed from its natural habitat and squeezed into a kind of art zoo. Faced with masterpiece after masterpiece I get wonderment fatigue and it takes something stupendous to stop me heading wearily for the tearoom. Hieronymus Bosch did it in the Prado with his little pale sinners in *The Garden of Delights*. It was impossible to believe they were 500 years old.

Some trips are special pilgrimages. In the 1950s I was taken to see Salvador Dali's *The Christ of St John of the Cross* in Glasgow. I had never heard of him (Dali, that is – I knew about Christ) or his surreal excesses and the picture, high and alone against a velvet background, seemed appropriately devout. In later years, the *Mona Lisa* was inevitably a disappointment behind her bulletproof glass but the *Night Watch* was big enough to stun from a distance. *Guernica* has a whole gallery wing to itself, the approach lined by Picasso's preliminary drawings for his spontaneous outburst of anger. It has two guards because people still get angry back.

Better than celebrity spotting, though, are surprises. Wandering around Hampstead Heath (with my wife), we took shelter from the rain in Kenwood House. There, only a few miles from the College, is a fabulous collection of paintings bought by one of the Guinness dynasty with profits from the family beverage, and bequeathed to the nation. (Er, yes – the British nation.) The house is small, relatively speaking – well, certainly more homely than the Hermitage – and attendants may chat knowledgeably about pictures you might otherwise overlook. The abiding memory, however, is coming face to face with Rembrandt. No crowds, just the two of you: him with his paintbrush and steady gaze, and you with your umbrella.

Moving pictures

Medical institutions would like to be patrons of the arts but, with prices as they are, it isn't easy. St Bartholomew's has fine 16th century portraits in its great hall but not, I imagine, in its outpatient departments. Anything nice in a hospital doesn't last long, even if nailed to the wall. Leeds Infirmary, having lost some fetching tapestry to someone with a good eye and a large screwdriver, has lined its main corridor with photographs. At least we'll still have the negatives.

Royal Colleges go in for contemporary portraiture. Smaller colleges are struggling a bit, aware they will run out of wall space before they run out of presidents, but our own has the perfect system, rotating its famous faces slowly around the room until, after 60 years, none of their former colleagues is still around to be upset by the portrait's relegation to the vaults. One sign of impending mortality is when you realise that three walls include people you have known personally.

Higher, and a bit to the left

Hanging pictures at home is a great test of the marriage bond but we have reached consensus with our eclectic collection of impulse buys. My favourite? Perhaps the little watercolour I spotted in a big display in

Edinburgh and insisted on buying. It turned out to be – no, not a Scottish Colourist, but a picture of the back of the house where my wife lived as a child. They can't teach you that at school.

Family history

There's a lot of interest in genealogy nowadays. On television we follow celebrities tracing their roots to far-flung places like Scotland or the Caribbean. In the papers we read of eccentric Italians who would have been English royalty had not some hasty law been passed in the 17th century. On the net are websites promising to help us find our ancestors. We do feel tempted. It's not so much the thought that we may be descended from somebody famous, it's just knowing where we come from.

Having an unusual name, though, takes away a lot of the mystery. It must be thrilling to be called Smith or Jones and hit the search button with at least a small chance of discovering that you are related to Delia or Arthur or Griff Rhys or Vinny. But if your surname is vanishingly rare it's over in an instant. One click on Google reveals all the family, including the Australians. Plus, in my case, a small German film company, Drife Productions, which I sincerely hope is artistic and high minded like the rest of us.

See ewe, Jimmy?

Some Scottish families clearly liked to travel. The McDonalds and the Campbells, for example, must have set out from the Old Country eager to sell hamburgers and canned soup to the world, with the result that nowadays they are all over the place. The Drifes, by and large, couldn't be bothered, or perhaps they felt that north Dumfriesshire is just so perfect, darling, that one can't possibly consider living anywhere else. Whatever the reason, our clan spent most of its history in the hills, quietly herding sheep. We whistled a lot but otherwise kept our heads down.

It is embarrassing to find that one has peace-loving ancestors. It denotes low social status. The upper classes like to point out that long ago their forefathers were mercenary cut-throats who fought battles up and down the land. Having murdered their rivals and built themselves a castle, the ancestors could relax and found a dynasty of benign toffs who collected antiques and bred chrysanthemums. Old family mottoes like *Mihi spectaculas* ("Are you looking at me?") are the only clues to their violent past. By contrast the Drife crest, *Sinister et sedente* ("Left a bit and sit down") refers, we think, to the shepherd's instructions to his Border collie.

Oral evidence

The fact that all our relatives lived in one area made it easy for my father to carry out genealogical studies. He would visit ageing aunts and listen to them reminisce over a cup of tea. To us children this seemed tedious in the extreme but I now realise it is respectable academic research. Members of the arts faculty are paid good money to do this kind of thing and may even get an allowance to jog the memory of the oldest inhabitant with pints of wallop. They grumble, of course, that their salary is meagre compared to that of a medical academic but when you think QALYs and then balance gynae outpatients against the saloon bar of The Fox and Marksman, it's a close call.

To be taken seriously, oral evidence has to come from very elderly people. Long-term memories suddenly become precious when we know we may lose them at any minute. In the prime of life, people's histories are boring. When my sister and I were children we would roll our eyes and yawn ostentatiously if our parents began a story with "During the war . . .". Now, too late, we realise they were eye-witnesses to one of history's greatest upheavals and we should have been taking notes. People often say that survivors of the First World War never spoke about it afterwards because they were so traumatised. Perhaps the real reason is that nobody would listen.

£6 well spent

Reassuringly, the advent of the internet validated my father's tea-based research. No rich uncle emerged from cyber-space and the Edwardian era's large families and high infant mortality were confirmed. What the web did do, though, was to bring me closer to my grandmother, who died after delivering stillborn triplets. For a modest fee, Scotland's General Register

Office has made marriage certificates (up to 1929) and death certificates (up to 1954) available electronically – and, preserving confidentiality, birth certificates up to 1904. (If you're 102, you don't mind who knows it.) Splashing out six quid with some misgivings, I found my grandparents' marriage lines. Seeing the young couple's details in careful copperplate was strangely moving. Then I downloaded granny's death certificate. I already knew she was one of the 3000 or so maternal deaths in 1927, when she was 42 and my father was 8. I knew from old sepia photographs that she was beautiful. But I hadn't realised that she died of flu and mitral incompetence. Aunts don't know everything, after all.

Life cycles

In our specialty we are used to biorhythms. Some are obvious, like the menstrual cycle. Some are obscure, like the nightly peak in the onset of normal labour. Some are impossible to understand, like the junior doctors' duty rota. Each of them rolls along inexorably, a primeval force of nature. Working at night makes you realise the power of diurnal rhythm. Or it did in the old days when we worked three-day weekends followed by normal Mondays. How far could we push ourselves before showing tell-tale signs of sleep deprivation — miscalculating drug doses, snapping at the consultant, nodding off during a hysterectomy? ('Lift Drife's head out of the wound, please, somebody, and smack it.')

In today's homogenised world, shifts are short and you can spend all night clubbing or Internet banking (on different nights, ideally). Overseas travel no longer depends on the tides. You can buy strawberries in November and watch *Match of the Day* over Sunday breakfast. You can take the pill. It's easy to think that technology has abolished biorhythms, but it hasn't.

Male cycles

Unlike the ovarian cycle, little research has been done on male biorhythms. In my psychosexual clinic I sometimes ask men how often they need sex. Needless to say, I never get a sensible answer. Nevertheless male cycles do exist.

The grooming cycle: Young men visit hairdressers frequently, worried that their scalp is getting too stubbly and anxious to regain that Matt Lucas look. The older male, by contrast, looks unnaturally shorn for one week in sixteen. For the next three months he looks normal and then suddenly his hair starts sticking out at right angles and obscuring his vision in high winds. The cycle ends when Sister makes personal remarks or he finds himself walking into lampposts.

The menswear cycle: This one is interesting because it does not exist. The idea of buying new clothes *before your old ones wear out* never occurs to men. Women hurry to the shops before a big social function but men do not freak out at the prospect of being seen in last year's dinner suit. If there are holes in it, perhaps…but it depends where the holes are.

The car cycle: This certainly does exist and affects both sexes. The decision to change one's car is made by a few hypothalamic neurones linked to one's biological clock, self-esteem centre and (loosely) financial centre. Next time a colleague gets a new car, ask him why. His answer will be a masterpiece of rationalisation.

Work cycles

Hospitals are affected by the rhythm of the working day, by pre- and post-weekend mood swings and by the annual parade of holidays, half-term breaks, training days, national conferences and anaesthetic department audit sessions. Someone calculated that a hospital is fully functional between 10 a.m. and 11 a.m. on the first Tuesday in October but I reckon that's optimistic. As well as these cycles, we doctors have our personal work rhythms.

The exam cycle: For decades we faced regular examinations. Initially these came at the end of term but at medical school sadistic educationists put them after the holidays or just before our elective in the Seychelles. There was always a clock ticking in our head showing how many weeks to the next exam. Now we can't live without them. This is why we start a family before sitting Membership. After we pass we still have the children's exams to worry about, thank goodness.

The rotation: Throughout our training, life consists of six-month jobs. No sooner have we settled into a hospital and discovered the best takeaway than we are off to pizzas new. The style of practice learnt as a trainee does not serve us well as a consultant. No longer is it enough to give every outpatient a six-month follow-up appointment. It's worth a try, though.

Consultant cycles: We used to have a yearly cycle of nine months' work and three months' argument when the Trust's money ran out. NHS reorganisation completely changed this. Now we have nine months' work and three months' argument when the PCT's money runs out. Our short-term cycles have also changed. Instead of the postman arriving once or twice a day, e-mails trickle in all the time. Trivial or apocalyptic, they must be read. The killer blow comes at 5 pm when secretaries everywhere stop work, click 'SEND ALL' and fill our screens with attachments.

The wrinkly years

The medical career cycle used to be easy to understand: a decade of exploitation, two decades of intensive private practice and five to ten years of reminiscing about the old days. Now, however, young and old are treated the same, with annual appraisals and goals. My goal? To boldly reminisce where no one has reminisced before. That's what we do at my stage of the cycle.

Doctor in t' house

It is now 15 years since we moved to Leeds – by far the longest period I have spent in one post. The same goes for my wife, though her general practice, with its purpose-built premises and on-line computers, is almost unrecognisable from a decade and a half ago. My hospital base has changed too – many more consultants and many fewer beds – but thank goodness the nurses and midwives are back in proper uniforms again, just like the old days.

Like most doctors, my wife and I have moved several times during our careers, though unspectacularly compared to some colleagues. We have not had to change continents or learn a new language, unless you count getting to grips wi' t'Yorkshire dialect.

As you can tell from my pronunciation, I still don't sound like a Yorkshireman and I don't suppose I ever shall. To be perfectly honest, I can't really tell the difference between Yorkshire and Lancashire when it cooms to speech patterns, but for heaven's sake don't tell anyone. I might be run out of town.

The white rose county

Yorkshire people are down-to-earth, friendly and warmhearted, but their rivalry with Lancastrians is a duty that has been passed down through the generations. It is a relationship unique among English counties. As far as I know, the inhabitants of, say, Hertfordshire and Bedfordshire don't profess mutual loathing, though perhaps they are just too polite to mention it to outsiders. The explanation for the Yorks/Lancs thing might be that the counties are separated by the Pennine Chain, so that the two peoples only met when they were tired and irritable after a very long walk. If so, the M62 should eventually spread peace and understanding.

But I fear it is deeper than that. I was not taught English history as a Scottish schoolboy but when I moved here I mugged up on the essentials, like the Plantagenet dynasties of 1154 –1485. The Plantagenets, originally French, made one of their princes Earl of Lancaster in 1265 and another Duke of York in 1385. The former chose a red rose and the latter a white rose as their emblems. A subsequent family feud over the royal succession went on for 30 years and became known as the Wars of the Roses. A romantic name, but thuggery nonetheless. Today, more than 500 years later, Manchester United play in red shirts and Leeds United in white.

Yorkshire medicine

Yorkshire's medical history is more uplifting and more recent. Treatment of the insane was revolutionised by William Tuke, a Quaker, who founded The Retreat Mental Hospital in York in 1796. It is still there, now specialising in up-market nervous disorders, I believe. Sir Thomas Clifford Allbutt, whom the Victorians liked to call the 'Father of Modern Medicine', was born in Dewsbury in 1836 and invented the clinical thermometer at

108

the age of 30 in Leeds. Much later he was appointed Regius Professor of Physic at Cambridge. In 1953 the first president of the Royal College of General Practitioners was Dr William Pickles, who had published ground-breaking papers on epidemiology from his rural practice in North Yorkshire. Earlier, back in 1926, Berkeley Moynihan had become president of the Royal College of Surgeons – only the second from outside London. Later he became the first Lord Moynihan and his marble bust still watches you as you climb the stairs of Leeds General Infirmary. Not Leeds *Royal* Infirmary, please note. We never asked for a Royal Charter. Still sulking, perhaps, after losing the Wars of the Roses.

House full

For some of us, the major non-medical attractions of Yorkshire are not its history, scenery or shops, splendid though these are, but its theatres. Two of the world's most successful living playwrights live on the Yorkshire coast. Alan Ayckbourn, a southerner, came to Scarborough in 1957 as an 18-year-old actor and was encouraged to write by Stephen Joseph, who had just founded a theatre there. Sixty-five plays, one knighthood and numerous London and Broadway hits later, Sir Alan is still running the Stephen Joseph Theatre in a converted Odeon cinema beside Scarborough railway station. He looks surprised and pleased if you tell him you enjoyed the evening's performance.

A few miles down the coast lives John Godber, miner's son and former teacher, whose 28 plays (so far) include *Up 'n' Under, Bouncers* and *On the Piste.* He has been Artistic Director of Hull Truck Theatre Company since 1984. Yorkshire-born, he does have a proper local accent and perhaps that is the reason, paradoxically, why his plays win awards and fill theatres all over the world. There are not many luvvies in Hull and his audiences are looking for a reet good night out. We know how to enjoy ourselves, us Yorkshire folk.

Speaking as a patient

One of the problems about being a male obstetrician and gynaecologist is that, no matter how empathic you are, you cannot fully put yourself in the patient's place. I remember as an SHO thinking I ought, just once, to lie on a delivery bed and put my ankles in the stirrups to find out what it feels like. Of course, I never did. I couldn't trust any of my colleagues to get me down again.

I suppose empathy is almost as difficult in some other specialties. My dim recollection of hospital admission for tonsillectomy does not include any trace of a surgeon, or a nurse, though we yelled for them. The main memory, apart from blood in my mouth, was of the American comics the boy in the next bed gave me: my first encounter with Spiderman, a hero much weirder than Dennis the Menace.

Under the knife

As a benign gynaecologist (if that's the right term) you can sympathise to some extent with your surgical patient if you've had an operation yourself. More so after two. My herniorrhaphy wound, in my teens, was closed with staples and I assumed removing them would need heavy engineering equipment. My appendectomy, at 21, was followed by relief on my part that a respectable reason had been found for my sudden aversion to beer, and by a belief on my colleagues' part that I could be taken back to the pub within 48 hours. This was not a good idea and may explain why I've been sceptical about early discharge ever since.

But losing an appendix isn't the same as losing an ovary or a womb. The nearest internal equivalent in the male is the prostate and we chaps don't want to talk about that, thank you. Our information on prostatic screening comes from Billy Connolly's graphic description of pelvic examination by a man with a rubber glove and, quite frankly, we'd rather die.

When it comes to perineal surgery, men haven't experienced this since barber-surgeons stopped cutting for stone. We shudder to think of anyone seeing that part of our anatomy. For me, the nearest the surgeons got to it was excising a pilonidal sinus just before Finals. (Was I a surgery addict or what?) Lying prone, all I saw of my surgeons was their shoes, which radiated an air of amused detachment. All I wanted was technical competence and, happily, that's what I got. I still meet one of them occasionally: I'm surprised he remembers my face.

Obstetric encounters

My first encounter with an obstetrician was in 1947, in a small nursing home. I don't know his name. Mother rarely spoke of him, though she occasionally mentioned her labour in hushed tones, commenting that the pain had been beyond her worst imaginings and adding kindly that I mustn't blame myself. Looking back I think we should have been more grateful to him and his forceps. Maternal mortality was 1 in 1000 and 15% of deaths occurred in maternity homes. Across England and Wales at least 60 women a year died of prolonged labour or traumatic delivery. So thanks, mister, for getting me out.

In the 1970s expectant fathers did not accompany their partners to the booking clinic. There was no real-time ultrasound to attract them. These days dads want to see the first scan but why they come to follow-up clinics remains a mystery to me. My emancipated wife did not want me in the corner during her consultations. And as an obstetric registrar I felt superfluous during her labours, particularly when the midwife was pushing the baby back to give the consultant time to arrive and do a normal delivery. Gosh, how things have changed.

Crumbling together

As you get older, gender differences seem less important but they don't disappear, as the NHS's disastrous experiment with mixed-sex wards proved. Mind you, when I spent time in a unisex intensive care unit I didn't bother about who was in the next bed. That admission was the result of spectacular travel-induced thromboembolism (have I shown you my CAT scan?) and, I notice, it was exactly seven years ago as I write. I'm not sure that it made me more sympathetic but it has at least cured me of any lingering desire to assume the lithotomy position.

No photos, please

Reading '*And finally...*' just got harder. As of January this year you must imagine the author's boyish smile, distinguished forehead and immaculately groomed beard without the help of that little photograph at the bottom of the page. Let me reassure you that the retro-chic bow tie and the dashing good looks are still in place, just as they were in 2005, and indeed in 1991, when the picture was taken.

Tides of fashion in medical publishing ebb and flow. For a few years authors' faces are cool but eventually the editor tires of all those startled mug shots from the photo booth in Tesco. Secretly, editors like to imagine their writers as glamorous creatures reclining in silk pyjamas, dictating clipped sentences to an earnest stenographer. They don't like being confronted with the ugly truth that articles are produced by people in paper hats, tapping at laptops between cases in the theatre coffee room.

Snapping doctors

Doctors are not, in any event, very image conscious and they generally feel uncomfortable about being photographed. This may date from an era when anonymity was essential and any hint of self-publicity was a breach of medical ethics. How quaint, indeed protectionist, that attitude seems to us now. These days, the public expects visibility and transparency and it is up to us to provide both simultaneously.

Some hospitals have photos of board members and senior managers near the main entrance. Wards and clinics often have pictures of slightly embarrassed nursing staff, but I have yet to see public photographs of doctors. Surely we should be out there, in charismatic black and white, looking wise, caring and inspiring. Admittedly, it will be hard work for the Trust to keep changing the display along with the rota and to spell our names correctly underneath, but visibility and transparency demand no less.

As you get older, photographs become essential as an *aide-mémoire*. When I was a trainee, a wise consultant had us snapped so he could remember who we were when we wrote later asking for references. The pictures lined his office. I wish I had done the same. Instead, my walls are decorated with group photos from conferences, like a sports club with its sepia triumphs of yesteryear. The RCOG HRT and Osteoporosis Study Group of 1990 may not have the same cachet as The Wembley Wizards of 1927, but the picture tugs at the academic heartstrings nonetheless.

Outside my office are photographs of past professors. The idea was to emulate ancient universities that have portraits going back several centuries. The Leeds chair, however, only became full-time in 1945 and as my predecessors were long-lived there are just two pictures, one on either side of the door. Alongside is a photo of the four consultants who looked after the whole of Leeds in the 1950s. One was a woman, who is said to have taken her dogs with her on ward rounds.

Compromising pictures

An ill-kept secret of mine is that out of office hours I am part of a cabaret group, which sometimes performs on the Edinburgh Festival Fringe. Publicity photos are an essential part of showbiz and in our heyday we used to make the front page of the local paper, thanks to a beautiful lady vocalist. The combination of a piano and a nurse's uniform produces genuine interest in the most jaded picture editor.

As our group dwindled to two male senior lecturers it became harder to excite the paparazzi, but just before I came to Leeds we produced the first of our farewell shows and I spent an hour or two with a photographer from a national broadsheet. Using a shop window, we contrived a shot in which my feet appeared to be in mid-air and I had two heads (older readers may remember a comedian called Harry Worth). On my first day in the new job here I noticed that my secretary had cut out the picture and stuck it on her filing cabinet, discreetly, but it stayed there for years.

New readers start here

If you are a first-time *TOG* reader you will be wondering what this article has been about. I'm sorry. It's just that I did enjoy being recognised over the canapés after the MRCOG admission ceremony. At the next one, I shall pencil *'And finally...'* at the top of my name badge and see if anyone notices.

Fine dining

What this journal needs is a restaurant critic. *TOG* does an excellent job of providing food for the mind, but readers have bodies too and their taste buds deserve education. Trainees cannot live by pizza alone, try though they might. As consultants, each will be expected to set an example of gracious living, so attention must be paid to their CPD (Continuing Palatal Development). A *TOG* column on upmarket eating and drinking would also benefit the wider community. It will boost the local economies of Gressingham, Aberdeen and Angus and help the journal by attracting classy advertisements: 'Embarrassing bladder irritation? Not if she sticks to 1999 Corton Grand Cru Clos de la Vigne au Saint.'

The science of dining out, like that of medicine, never stands still. How often have we been disappointed to discover, on returning to a cosy trattoria much loved in our student days, that it is now a kebab shop or the Funny Woks Jumbo Takeaway? Keeping readers updated nationwide will be hard work if *TOG* can afford only one inspector. He or she will have to be based near the centre of the UK – somewhere like, say, Leeds – and should be a doctor, able to switch painlessly between cordon bleu and the hospital canteen. For the work load to be manageable, the column must be limited to the very top eateries.

Splashing out

Not that I wish to push myself forward, but I am one of the few people qualified for the job. I have the ability, rare among Scotsmen, to enjoy mind-bogglingly expensive food without suffering a dry mouth and sphincter failure. It is a skill acquired through arduous practice and my training has included some sticky moments. Only in 2003, in a temple of *haute cuisine* overlooking Notre Dame, a waiter handed me a wine list the size of a telephone directory, with prices in four figures. As many an old campaigner will tell you, feeling afraid is OK: what matters is how you deal with it. With the sweat trickling into my collar, I turned the pages and found a cheap(ish) 1973 red. 'Bring me this,' I told the waiter: 'Nous sommes celebrating our pearl anniversary.' My wife and I gazed adoringly at each other, trying to ignore his eyebrows.

But prohibitive prices are unusual. Generally, you don't need a bank loan but simply the right mindset, which means deciding that tonight is a special occasion. The College diary is a big help here. 'Let's look at the sweet trolley, darling. After all, today is the day that Mrs Ann Edson Taylor went over Niagara Falls in a barrel in 1901.' Or you could enlist the help of the waiter: 'Which cheese would you recommend to mark the 576th anniversary of the capture of Joan of Arc? Hard cheddar, perhaps?'

Dining alone

Restaurant critics often work in pairs. 'My companion ordered the rock oysters while I chose the tomato soup. Beware the croutons, which I found disappointingly under toasted.' I suspect the verdict on the meal depends more on the conversation and attractiveness of the workmate than on the efforts of the chef. The conscientious *TOG* inspector will concentrate better if dining alone, but this too requires practice.

Solo dining is difficult whatever your gender. A female lone diner can maintain an air of Garboesque mystery by gazing coolly into the distance but men prefer to look busy. The male lone diner equips himself with page proofs and, in case his red pen runs dry, a paperback. A difficult crossword used to be ideal but nowadays *The Times* comes in so many sections that when you finally find the right page the floor around your chair is littered with newsprint, as if you were a secret agent taking precautions against a surprise attack.

TOG awards

Some day, I hope, leading restaurants will proudly display *TOG* awards beside their AA rosettes. The journal should develop a system of symbols for its restaurant page. A little laparoscope will mean 'merits a look', while a pair of crossed forceps means 'worth swapping your on-call for'. A College crest, with its light and dark background, means the establishment gets a star for both lunch and dinner. Michelin men, with their spare tyres, will seem passé and the world will assume that *TOG* means 'The Old Gastronome'.

The sports page

I'm still on a mission to boldly go where no medical journal has gone before, so what about a sports section? *TOG*'s readership is international and so is sport, particularly the English Premiership. On holiday this summer in northwest Iceland my wife and I saw a local lad in a soccer shirt with 'ROONEY' on the back. On my last visit to Kuala Lumpur there was a giant David Beckham in the window of the Manchester United shop. More than music or the web, football brings people together.

Wherever you are in the world, your taxi driver will grin if you mention Leeds United. I watched some home games years ago but I've never really got the hang of spectating. Goals tend to be scored while I'm reading the programme and, even when I concentrate, the ball moves faster than the eye can follow. I lack the earthy wit and appropriate vocabulary for hurling abuse at the referee and when it comes to Mexican waves, my timing is rubbish.

The hospital league

My lack of skill must have disappointed my mother, who travelled from Scotland all the way to Cardiff to give birth so that I could qualify to play for Wales. (She was Welsh, incidentally – she wasn't trying to sabotage the opposition.) Unfortunately she took me back to Scotland, a country with a serious inferiority complex where the crowd sings a lament before every rugby international. Had I stayed in Wales, who knows? I might have been Jinking Jim, the Pride of Pontypridd.

But I'm not bitter. Like everyone else, I'm an expert when watching sport on the box, shouting advice from the sofa to Tiger Woods or Paula Radcliffe. Sport on television bridges generation gaps and sport in real life does the same. Chatting to junior medical students you discover a world of inter-university leagues and local cricket teams, and occasionally you meet someone who shyly admits to competing at national level. But most have given this up by the time they graduate.

We should encourage them to carry on. Hospitals, like nations and towns, should have their own teams to support through thick and thin. This would bond the staff and deflect criticism from middle management. The

NHS could sponsor inter-hospital leagues instead of messing about with star ratings. Lacrosse for midwives, perhaps, and golf (naturally) for consultants. Or, better, multidisciplinary teams with specialist backup from in-house physiotherapists and orthopaedic surgeons.

Sportsmen's dinners

Besides keeping players fit and boosting morale, sport promotes foreign travel, provides work for the makers of face paint and Styrofoam hands, and gives an excuse for black-tie dinners. I've been to a few of these, sometimes speaking on behalf of medical charities. No matter how polished your material, you are sure to be outdone by the guest of honour, a sporting icon of yesteryear looking back on his or her career with humorous insights into famous victories or defeats.

As a visiting speaker from another planet, anxious to blend in, you may be tempted to try the same. 'Then there was the classic Headingley hysterectomy of '76. I wasn't feeling too well as I had a bit of a gippy tummy that day. The anaesthetist was a big, mean fellow, known to one and all as "Mick the Mask", and the theatre sister, Tiny Trisha, had to stand on a box. Suddenly ...'

My advice is, don't do it. The audience won't smile, I promise you.

Another record tumbles

Numeracy skills are honed by sport, particularly cricket. So little happens on the field that the main excitement for fans comes from checking the archives and discovering that today's average of 9.736 runs per over is the highest by a fifth-wicket partnership on a Wednesday since the legendary TCP Wythenshawe retired in 1910.

Looking at my own scorecard, I see I've just completed my 50th successive back page – 30 for *TOG* and 20 for its predecessor, *The Diplomate*. I believe this is the highest total ever reached by a left-handed Scotsman in Yorkshire, but the record awaits ratification. So how was it done? Well, you have to treat the word processor with respect and really, y'know, just take each paragraph as it comes. And how do I feel about the record? Well, I owe it all to a great team of editors and typesetters, but naturally I'm over the moon.

Deadline in Dushanbe

Many people enjoy flying. Thanks to low-cost airlines, you can pop over to Prague for the weekend or even spend a few days shopping in New York. This is not my idea of a good time. I dislike airports, with their stone-faced immigration officials and their offensive assumption that I'm wearing explosive shoes. In the plane I brood about what could go wrong – missed connections, thromboembolism, acute psychosis on the flight deck – and prepare for the worst. Believe me, I'm not a cheery travelling companion. When I reach my hotel, though, I lighten up, particularly if it is in an exotic city never before visited by anyone from Leeds. Such places are few. When I remarked last month to a midwife that I was going to Bishkek she replied that Kyrgyzstan is beautiful and she loves the Silk Road. Well, I'm writing this in Dushanbe, Tajikistan and I hope you're impressed. If you're thinking 'That's where our team lost 2-0 against Locomotiv Tajik and we had that iffy curry', please don't say so.

The WHO on tour

I'm here with the World Health Organization (WHO), whose initials are less global than you think. In French they are OMS (Organisation Mondiale de la Santé) and in Germany the Weltgesundheitsorganisation is, presumably, known as 'W'. Our team (an Italian, a Dane, a German and myself) communicate well enough in English but doctors here speak Russian. Our interpreters do an amazing job (surely it's neurologically impossible to listen in one language while speaking in another) and add a touch of romance to our talks. 'Accoucheur' and 'reanimator' sound far grander than 'obstetrician' and 'intensivist' and wouldn't any surgical team prefer to be a 'theatre brigade'?

We arrive at meetings laden with laptops, memory sticks, CDs, extension leads and mysterious Cyrillic handouts of our presentations. In the past, lecturers turned up with a flip chart or a box of slides. Now we're starting to look like a Rolling Stones world tour, though our budget does not extend to roadies. A local technician silently connects our computers to his projectors and once we start speaking, the audience put on their

118

headphones. This means they don't notice when their mobile phones go off. Even here, Mozart and Strauss are big in the ringtone business.

What, no College?

Despite the technology, countries in the south of the former USSR are horribly poor. Doctors' salaries are $20 per month, so 'informal' payments by patients are normal in some specialties, particularly ours. There is a brain drain to Russia and Kazakhstan (which, whatever Borat says, is comparatively well off). But some problems are more familiar. Ministries rigidly control clinical practice with unhelpful diktats. Professional organisations are weak or non-existent. Doctors are terrified of disciplinary procedures. If you want to see where the NHS is heading, come to Central Asia…but not as a patient.

Our hosts are astute people and generous. Last night at a PECTOPAH (restaurant – I worked it out) the meal was punctuated by toasts while a band in the corner played The Beatles. Toasts here are for real. If you fail to drain your glass of vodka you are benignly chided. It's a good system for making friends. When you're the eighth diner to make a speech, there is no place for irony. You extol your colleagues, their patients, their country and world peace with deep sincerity, all the while hoping you don't slide off your chair before you finish.

Over the mountains

At the weekend we flew from Bishkek to Dushanbe—two hours over snowy mountains, near the highest peak in the former Soviet Union. We had been told that the airline was banned from Europe on safety grounds so you can imagine my mood of sunny good humour as we joined the queue to board the elderly Russian aeroplane. I spent the whole flight watching the propellers.

Dushanbe turned out to be a pleasant city with trees, boulevards and neo-Mogul style buildings. Tajiks originally came from Persia. Women wear vibrant colours and people are gentle and reserved, even in the markets. We liked the place immediately. Nevertheless, Tajikistan is at the bottom of the region's health league, so let's hope this week's workshop on maternity care goes well. This is no time to relax, folks. It's only a few days until the flight home and oh no, it's starting to snow.

119

Irish nights

A few months ago the College held an Irish Night. It drew a good crowd of Fellows and Members – many of them relieved, I suspect, that for once in late January they did not have to attend a Burns supper, so there would be no need to eat haggis or drink Scotch whisky. Other than that, none of us knew what to expect. Would there be readings from *Finnegans Wake* instead of *Tam O'Shanter*? What should we wear? The invitation said 'black tie' but surely something green was required? Do Irishmen wear kilts and, if so, could you hire one?

Most of us had pleasant, if hazy, memories of Irish nights in Ireland. One of my first, in the 1980s, was a meeting of the Irish Family Planning Association in the Limerick Inn. In those days contraception was still illegal south of the border and I was surprised that a Family Planning Association existed. Indeed, I thought my invitation was a hoax as it was signed 'Doctor Darling' and sent from 'Stillorgan'. Both turned out to be genuine (Stillorgan being a suburb of Dublin) and I spent a delightful night supping Guinness with resilient lady doctors as they swapped stories of court appearances.

Inspecting Wexford

Twenty years on, Ireland oozes sophistication. My wife and I have a weakness for posh hotels, smoke-free pubs, culture and Georgian architecture, so it's lucky that Dublin is only an hour away by air. Across Merrion Square from the National Maternity Hospital is Restaurant Patrick Guilbaud. Despite its name, it has nothing to do with family planning but does have two Michelin stars. North of the River Liffey, adjacent to the Rotunda Hospital, is the Gate Theatre, where we saw *Shining City* by Conor McPherson, a playwright now famous far beyond Dublin. Its ending was such a shock that we had to calm our nerves with stout in the nearest smoke-free environment.

Irish people have a knowledgeable, unpretentious attitude to the arts. In Dublin they speak respectfully of James Joyce while giving the impression that he was a friend of the family. Further down the coast, a little town serves up obscure European operas every October. Have you heard of *La*

Vestale by Mercadante? Neither had we until a couple of years ago but now we know that it wrings your withers as hero and heroine expire tragically in Act III. The Wexford Opera Festival was started in 1951 by a local doctor and is now world famous. There's something magical about eating fish and chips near the harbour with a Russian chamber choir squeezed around the next table.

They think it's all over

Further up the coast is Belfast – world famous, too, as the birthplace of the Titanic and the home of the Editor-in-Chief of *TOG*. It has two airports, the larger being about 20 miles out of town. Once (I know the date: it was 26 May 1999), there wasn't a taxi in sight when I arrived. I found the drivers huddled round a wireless and persuaded one to take me to my hotel. As we headed off with the car radio on, I realised this was the night of the European Cup Final. In the city centre I got to a television as the game reached full time, with Bayern Munich one goal up. And then...the memory of Manchester United scoring twice in extra time will live forever, even for a man from Leeds. Belfast went wild. I don't understand why they are United fans, but I suppose it's something to do with George Best.

The Irish are coming

So many good times. Such great hospitality: north and south. But how would the 'craic' transfer to Regent's Park? Very well, actually. We started in the lecture theatre with a marvellous young tenor who sang about the futility of the Troubles and ended with 'Danny Boy'. I must have heard it hundreds of times but it moved me to tears. At dinner our guest, the President of Ireland, said the last time she saw so many obstetricians she came away with twins. A hilarious raconteur followed her and then a virtuoso fiddler gave the first Elvis impersonation seen in Nuffield Hall. Or so I assume. We don't know what the Officers get up to when we aren't there.

Pushing sixty

It isn't the done thing to talk about your age and still less to go on about it in print, but senior consultants should be allowed to bend the rules sometimes. Besides, getting old is *à la mode* right now. This week's UK pop sensation, The Zimmers, may still be around when this issue reaches you, although I won't bet on it as the lead singer is 90 and several members are centenarians. The group was put together for a documentary about elderly folk who feel isolated. They now have a cult following – mainly, I suspect, people of my age exhilarated by the idea of life beyond the bus pass.

My age? Well, you've seen the title. I shall soon be eligible for free off-peak travel anywhere in Leeds, although I gather one has to share the bus with other people. There are downsides, however. You feel old-fashioned but can't change your ways. You still wear a cardigan, end your emails 'Yours sincerely' and you're irascible. Queues in banks and post offices, mobiles on trains, airport security – how does your blood pressure stand it? You mutter loudly, 'I don't believe it!' as your fellow sufferers look away.

A boomer's book

Still, we post-war baby boomers have been a lucky generation. As teenagers we were the first to discover The Beatles, so pop music has been an anticlimax ever since. At university we lived off government grants, so no debt for us. As obstetric trainees we were left alone, supported by a consultant on the phone. Later we decided it was illogical to stop doing obstetrics as soon as our training was complete and argued for consultant presence on the labour ward. So now we're back, nearly 60 and still pushing.

Some aspects of maternity care are timeless but change does happen. I still have my neatly typed MRCOG book from 1977. It reads like an obstetric supplement to the Domesday Book: 'Placenta praevia diagnosed by examination under anaesthesia … vaginal delivery of a footling breech in a primigravida…lytic cocktail…total dose infusion…pelvic assessment at booking…six-day postnatal stay'. Of the 25 obstetric patients, only one was over 30 – a woman having her ninth baby. Is Edinburgh still like that, I wonder?

122

Communication skills

Talking to patients gets easier as you get older. They warm to you because you look comfortable and don't use jargon, but they feel particularly reassured if you have a registrar nearby to keep you right.

Talking to younger colleagues is a joy but you feel that they come from a different world. With trainees, there's only so much you can say about MTAS and none of it is helpful or original. With students, you are genuinely interested but when you ask questions you sound like a sociologist doing fieldwork. With both groups, it's impossible to avoid reminiscing about your own youth but that is always a mistake. You're still not old enough for it to be interesting.

At medical meetings, sooner or later we wrinklies begin huddling together. You notice us adopting strange postures around the buffet, in an attempt to minimise the low backache and sciatica that strike when we stand holding a glass of wine and a Scotch egg simultaneously. The hot topic of conversation is likely to be the quality of the latest obituary. Believe me, you can't rely on The Daily Telegraph any more.

All together now

Your interest in music increases again with age. Of course you like opera, the grander the better, and occasionally you sneak out to see some 60s icon in a golden oldies road show. But you also start to become disinhibited and rediscover the lost pleasure of making your own music. Some of my friends are in madrigal groups and one is a member of the Really Terrible Orchestra, which claims that its gigs rapidly sell out because audiences find its honesty refreshing.

I don't think I've led up to this in quite the right way, but I must end with a plug for the next appearance of our own cabaret group, live on stage at the Edinburgh Fringe in August. Look out for The Secret Life of Robert Burns, with a section on how the Scots invented rock and roll. Our biggest problem is remembering the words, but if The Zimmers can do it, so can we.

Sharing a joke

I like jokes but professors are expected to be serious. The successful doctor should have a furrowed brow and ambitious trainees would be well advised to exercise their frontalis muscles regularly. Deaneries could issue instructions like the ones about pelvic floor exercises: 'You can do this sitting at your desk. Think about the rota for 30 seconds. Then relax. Think about your logbook for another 30 seconds. Then relax. Do this as often as you like. Within a few weeks you will notice a difference. You will have frown lines and people will treat you with respect.'

Beneath the consultant's grim exterior, however, lurks a wicked sense of humour. Or at least, that's what we like to think. After all, the juniors laugh at our jokes, provided they recognise them. Deep down we know this owes more to their politeness than to our comic timing but we still enjoy it. As long as the SpR is smiling, the consultant is happy. (But please, SpRs, don't overdo it.)

Anaesthetists and Scotsmen

Long ago, when I was a senior lecturer, jokes were straightforward. Your anaesthetist provided a fresh supply each week, generally about an Englishman, a Scotsman and an Irishman or perhaps the number of orthopaedic surgeons needed to change a lightbulb. Then things started to change. Comic stereotypes slowly became unacceptable unless they were Frenchmen or NHS managers. And your anaesthetist began to disappear behind ever-larger anaesthetic machines and finally stopped talking to you altogether.

So now, instead of jokes we have witty banter. The Irish are masters of this (think Terry Wogan or Neil McClure) but Scotsmen like me are at a serious disadvantage. Our sense of humour is often described as 'pawky', an Old Norse word meaning 'non-existent'. Sydney Smith, an English cleric who worked in Edinburgh around 1800, famously commented, 'It requires a surgical operation to get a joke well into a Scotch understanding'. Later, a Scots character in a play by JM Barrie responded: 'What beats me, Maggie, is how you could insert a joke with an operation'.

Highs and lows

I've always enjoyed epigrams. As a boy I was a fan of the American journalist HL Mencken, who wrote quips like: 'Conscience is the inner voice that warns us somebody is looking' and 'Every decent man is ashamed of the government he lives under'. The art is not dead and the new edition of *The Oxford Dictionary of Modern Quotations* has some gems, including: 'The email of the species is more deadly than the mail' (Stephen Fry, 2001) and an observation attributed to Peter Kay: 'All castles had one major weakness. The enemy used to get in through the gift shop'.

But putting jokes onto paper is a hit-or-miss business. You can't wink at readers to hint that they shouldn't take the next bit seriously and the feedback you get can be depressing. Years ago, when the fad for water birth first appeared, I thought I would satirise it by writing an article on 'Caesarean section under water'. In deadpan prose, I described how the technique had been invented in an operating theatre with faulty plumbing. I paid tribute to the assistant who had succumbed because there were only enough oxygen masks for the surgeon, anaesthetist and midwife. After publication I received a request for details about this important new procedure.

Students and patients

When you're teaching you have to ration your jokes. It's boring to tell the same ones to every new group but you can't be too spontaneous because it confuses the students. What joy, though, when you discover someone who is on your wavelength. Medical educationists talk about the 'appropriate use of humour', a heartsink phrase that takes away your will to live or to work in a modern medical school. Humour isn't a tool to be selected cold-bloodedly like a Langenbeck retractor. It bubbles up from within and sometimes escapes despite your best efforts... (no simile here, I think).

It's possible, but risky, to joke in the consulting room. Last week I was taking consent from a tricky patient. As I filled in the vast form with all the things we might do in the theatre, one of her companions said, 'She's thinking about getting married'. I murmured, 'Not under the same anaesthetic'. The patient was the one who laughed the loudest. Phew!

Peerless reviewers

Many application forms these days ask you to list publications in 'peer-reviewed' journals. What does this phrase mean? 'Peer-reviewed' does not indicate that all manuscripts are checked by Lord Patel or Lord Winston, but rather that they are scrutinised by people in the same field of research. 'Peer' means equal; but some peer reviewers are more equal than others. When I was young they were all called 'referees' but over the years they have changed their job title like everyone else. Theatre orderlies are now 'operating department practitioners', senior house officers are 'FY2s' and consultants are 'senior healthcare delivery operatives'. (Am I joking? I'm not sure.) In the world of medical publishing, editors are now 'editors-in-chief' and referees are 'reviewers'. Authors, however, are still 'authors'. Surely we can come up with something more trendy – 'sentence technicians', perhaps, or 'words R us'?

The author's view

As an author you are not supposed to know who the referees are, though anonymity may be compromised if one of them complains that you have failed to cite several important papers, all written by the same person. Occasionally a reviewer simply makes approving noises but more often he or she asks you to alter your carefully crafted manuscript. You then form a mental image of a miserable ogre with no sense of proportion and a badly flawed knowledge of statistics.

But you play the game and you agree to some of the changes. For the remainder, you give long and detailed explanations of why your original version was correct. Your covering letter expresses surprise that the journal is still using a reviewer who has clearly lost his or her marbles and ought not to be let out of the house without a minder. It's best to tear this up and write a polite one.

The sad life of the reviewer

When asked to review a paper yourself you look at the deadline, say yes and then forget all about it. This used to make refereeing a leisurely business. Eventually the journal would start sending reminder letters by second-class post until, full of guilt, you sent off your report with profuse apologies. With the internet, all this has changed. Some journals email a tactful reminder as the deadline approaches. You now complete your report on screen, ticking the small boxes and typing comments in the big ones. It's like an MTAS* application, except that you are expected to write something intelligent.

Refereeing is usually hard work. It used to involve a trip to the library to check the literature. Few papers are completely original and most authors are not very good at explaining what has been done before and what their study adds. Even now, with the internet, it is not always easy to find the previous papers that inspired the present one. Woe betide the author if they do not appear in the list of references. Then you work your way through it, page by page, sometimes asking for more data, sometimes suggesting improvements, sometimes losing the will to live. You try to ignore the fact that this is a labour of love. Payment? You must be joking. Sleep? Who needs it?

In the editor's chair

As editor – even as editor-in-chief – your power is limited. In the old days, you could exert subtle influence by choosing the referees yourself, knowing which were hawks and which were doves. Again, the internet has changed all this. The journal office allocates the papers, discovering reviewers you have never heard of. One of the editor's arcane pleasures is comparing the opinions of strangers in, say, the Far East and Central Europe and finding that, although their styles of English are widely different, their views are reassuringly similar.

Readers are unaware of all this and so they should be. Like restaurant hygiene or aircraft maintenance, people expect it and don't want to know the details, but they get very upset if things go wrong. When a paper is well edited, nobody notices – not even the author, who never says thank you for sorting out the ambiguous wording, tortured grammar and incorrect punctuation. From time to time, though, a grateful author realises that the peer-review process has improved the paper considerably and asks for this to be acknowledged to the reviewer. This is the other arcane pleasure – giving a warm glow (you hope) to the anonymous benefactor.

[*MTAS: *The Medical Training Application Service, a national system for online job applications by doctors in training, was set up in 2007, caused widespread chaos and distress and was shelved.*]

Mystic Jim's predictions

An obstetrician's job involves foretelling the future. It didn't always. Until a century ago, obstetrics was reactive, not proactive. A boy would arrive breathlessly and shout, 'Come quickly, doctor, the midwife says you're needed!'. The obstetrician would summon the pony and trap and hasten to the home confinement, hoping to rescue mother, baby and midwife with as little loss of life as possible.

Then came antenatal care. In the 1900s, it was a good idea to try and diagnose problems like rickets or heart disease before labour began. Over the years, however, people began to believe that simply by seeing a woman at the start of pregnancy we could tell what would happen at the end. We can't, of course. Nevertheless, we give women odds, like bookies, on everything from chromosome abnormality to caesarean section. We fondly imagine this is helpful to them.

Developing second sight

Playing the odds works most of the time. In late pregnancy, a doctor or midwife can palpate an abdomen (no matter how obese) and write 'presentation cephalic' in the notes with a 96% probability of being right. During labour, the odds on guessing the correct position of the fetal head are less favourable. As today's trainees have few opportunities to learn by actually examining women in labour, supernatural powers are becoming necessary.

Those of us with Celtic ancestry have an advantage here. With a Welsh mother and a Shetlandic grandmother (not to mention Cornish blood on my wife's side) I was always likely to have second sight. And so it has proved. As I gaze at the board in the labour ward ('8 cm at 1 a.m. 9 cm at 3 a.m. Fully dilated at 5 a.m. Commenced pushing at 7 a.m.') I begin to see visions. A picture of an operating table forms itself in front of my misty old eyes. My uncanny predictions really impress the team.

Horizon scanning

Now the time has come for me to offer my gift more widely to the profession. Government departments and Royal Colleges have to look into the future but, poor things, they try to do so by forming committees or consulting focus groups. There is no need for such expensive and unproven methods. Mystic Jim is here to advise on future trends. Here are a couple of examples:

Gold braid ahead

Remember when someone decided that midwives should dress in ordinary clothes rather than uniforms? This led to confusion in the wards when everyone wore identical T-shirts and elasticated trousers. You could usually tell patients from midwives by looking at their abdomens but sometimes embarrassing mistakes occurred. Eventually, patients said they preferred staff to look professional; midwives were given smart uniforms and everyone was happy again.

Mystic Jim predicts the same for doctors. 'Bare below the elbows' will not be enough for the Department of Health, who will decide that shirts are vectors of disease and, for good measure, will make us wear headbands. When we all look like Rab C Nesbitt, patients will rebel. They will insist upon us looking like proper doctors and will go further, demanding ways of distinguishing FY2s from increasingly youthful consultants. So we shall all wear jackets again, with one line of gold braid at the cuffs for SpRs, two lines for consultants and epaulettes for professors.

Double your numbers

We've learned much in recent years from the airline industry, including simulated training and 'near miss' reporting, but we have yet to introduce their most basic safety measure. All flights have not only a pilot but also a co-pilot, who checks on procedures and can take over in the event of sudden illness.

Mystic Jim predicts the same for labour wards. Twenty-four hour consultant presence will soon involve not just one obstetrician but two— consultant and co-consultant. I'm not predicting more heart attacks (which will still be rare and most likely to occur during management meetings) but this change will be required for risk management. Consultant and co-consultant will constantly observe one another's performance, support each other and maintain a non-stop written record on their shared PalmPilot®.

It's tough being a visionary. Sometimes we're not taken seriously. Twenty years ago my prediction of a "consultant-delivered" service was greeted with hilarity but now it is happening. So take note, workforce planners. Many a true word is spoken in jest.

Fourteen years in the chamber

Actually, I'm not certain that it was 14 years. At my age these things get a bit blurred. I know that I joined the RCOG Council a long time ago, in the mid-1990s, when I was already quite old. I began as a Fellows' representative, you see, never having stood for election as a Member. The idea hadn't occurred to me. Just as well—I couldn't have coped. Members' representatives are mature beyond their years. In Council they talk in well-modulated sentences and effortlessly convey the moral authority of those who speak on behalf of the real workers.

I am certain, however, about when my stint on Council ended. It was a month ago, when eight or nine of us (none of us is quite sure) left the Council chamber with the President's benediction ringing in our ears. Though come to think of it, our last farewell wasn't in the chamber at all. A man with a drill was building the new Domus on the top floor and couldn't be persuaded to stop, so our final Council meeting was in one of those strange glass-fronted rooms in the education centre. We made our dignified exit and then got lost trying to find the stairs.

Moving with the times

When I first joined Council it met on Saturday mornings and had about thirty-five members (mainly men), who were required to wear gowns but could discard them after the coffee break. Fourteen years on, all this still applies except that Council now meets on Friday afternoons as well. This constancy does not represent slavish adherence to tradition. Over the years, president after president arrived filled with reforming zeal and tried to persuade us to meet on a weekday or even take our jackets off in summer. Their proposals were thoroughly debated and politely rejected. Some things have changed. Council papers used to be sent out by post. A week before each meeting a huge envelope would arrive, sealed with industrial-strength glue. Recently we got worried about our carbon footprint and now our desktops grunt, just like the postman, as the mother of all attachments arrives by email. It generally includes a full copy of this month's government plan for reforming the NHS (not to be confused with last month's). Few of us have the nerve to ask a secretary to print out the whole lot, so now we all turn up with laptops and sit half-hidden from the President's gaze behind a stockade of screens.

Do join us—I mean, them

If all this makes you want to stand for Council, here are some hints on getting started. Electioneering is not allowed, so don't try to organise US-style caucuses with placards and balloons. Negative campaigning is, in any case, impossible because you never know who the other candidates are until the ballot papers are sent out. When you discover that they are old friends who are smarter than you, it's too late.

At your first Council meeting you are expected to keep quiet. Doing so indicates that you are biding your time and sizing up your fellow councillors, and makes them nervous. You will be tempted to continue this policy indefinitely but you really should say something eventually, even if it's only goodbye. At your second meeting the big decision is where to sit. Choosing the left or right has no political significance but depends mainly on whether you prefer to look at the picture of the Queen Mother or stare out of the window.

Don't make big speeches. In some councils I could mention, members would regularly launch into Churchillian orations, pausing briefly at the start to acknowledge that all their points had already been made. Mercifully, RCOG councillors keep their comments brief—just long enough to ensure that the officers are fully informed about the views of the obstetrician on the Clapham omnibus and the gynaecologist in the BMW.

Demob happy

After 14 years (or thereabouts) you will look around the chamber and decide you are the oldest person there. Beware of mentioning this. Several other councillors will think they are more senior, leading to pointed exchanges over coffee. At your last few meetings you will feel tempted to give Council the benefit of your wisdom on every item on the agenda. Resist that temptation. Keep mum until you leave. Then write an article.

The art of assisting

Assisting in theatre is an undervalued skill these days, without even its own module in the College's training manual. In fact, it isn't mentioned there at all as far as I can see, though I may have missed it among all those abbreviations (OP: 'Occipitoposterior'; OOP: 'Out of programme'; OOPS: 'I've dropped the forceps'). Or perhaps it's supposed to be covered by the boxes marked OBSERVED PROCEDURE. Observing, however, is only a small part of this complex art.

Happy days in general surgery

Assisting has changed with the advent of the video-laparoscope. Forget laparoscopy's other so-called breakthroughs, like converting an 8 cm incision into four 'keyholes', each 2 cm long. The real advance is that assistants can now see what is going on. This must have transformed life for trainees in general surgery. In the old days, being second assistant at a cholecystectomy was as close as you could get to penal servitude. Your arms ached, all you could see was the back of somebody's head, and the surgeon kept complaining that your retractor was in the wrong place. Only the insanely ambitious came back for more.

Surgical SHOs, as we were called then, usually assisted the registrar as they got their first taste of that special, hands-across-the-table relationship. In my pre-FRCS days, general surgical registrars tackled almost all emergencies without bothering the consultant. One memorable Saturday the registrar and I (the SHO) replaced an abdominal aortic aneurysm with a Y-shaped knitted tube and I had to do the stitching on one side. It was life-or-death stuff and the registrar's comments were uninhibited. Today it might be called a bonding experience. (The patient survived, otherwise I wouldn't be telling you about it.)

Listen, laugh and learn

Our specialty is much less aggressive. I realised this as a student in the 1960s, soaking up the sights, sounds and smells of theatre for the first time. A consultant gynaecologist told me to scrub, stand on a box and cling onto some instruments while he did mysterious things to the pelvic floor. What I remember are his anecdotes. It is important to laugh at the chief's jokes but you need special skill to convey amusement while wearing a mask and keeping the forceps steady. I realised I had that talent and I cultivated it.

Is it still legal for students to act as assistants? I hope so, but nowadays they are elbowed out of the way by postgraduates hungry for operative experience. And we consultants have, sadly, become more serious. Instead of telling jokes we explain the difference between evidence-based operating and what we do in real life. Some of us, for example, open the peritoneum properly, rather than having a tug-of-war with the assistant, like Superman and the Incredible Hulk. And we close it again. Some day the evidence will lose its bias and back us up.

Take your partners

Modern rotas make it hard to achieve the bonding I remember from my weekend with the left common iliac artery. Today, whenever you go to theatre you are paired with somebody new, like a surgical equivalent of Scottish country dancing (where they change partners every eight bars). This is a pity. Assistants need time to get to know each surgeon's little ways. Some operators require an encouraging word to help them decide that haemostasis really is complete. And there is always a place for that sharp intake of breath when the surgeon heads towards dangerous territory.

Well-practised teamwork guards against absent-mindedness ('Er - don't you usually tie the vessel first, sir?') and makes operating a pleasure. But in any partnership, stresses can appear. In the old days senior registrars often spent a little too long on the firm, observing the boss's foibles. They were at their most entertaining when about to leave: 'How would you like me to cut your stitches today, sir? Too long or too short?'.

The teaching assistant

An essential role of the assistant is keeping the consultant up to date. Circulating round the region, trainees pick up techniques and quietly pass them on, like carriers. We consultants rarely admit we're learning something new. Assisting the trainee is a demanding art but our biggest challenge is at the end of training, when we are now required to sit next door in the coffee room while the trainee operates and tells all the jokes.

Fifty years BT

TOG may be 10 years old but it's a long way from having a bus pass. As one of the few contributors entitled to free bus travel, it falls to me to put *TOG*'s first decade into a wider historical perspective. Trainees may find it hard to imagine life in the era BT (Before *TOG*), so here is a brief summary of the preceding half-century. For added authenticity, I have based it on personal experience, which is valued by historians almost as much as it is scorned by medical science.

The 1940s

I missed most of this decade because I wasn't born yet but its final years left a deep impression. The 'demob' suit (civilian clothes given to soldiers on demobilisation after the Second World War) must have imprinted itself on my infant mind because I have always regarded a dark jacket and shapeless trousers as the height of fashion. Television history may give the impression that in the 1950s we were all Teddy boys and in the sixties, seventies and eighties we moved from beads to flares to platform heels. Not so. Like most of my medical contemporaries, my style hasn't changed since I was a first-year student.

The 1950s

These were tough times and the hardest part for me was realising that if I wanted to do medicine, I had to give up woodwork. Our village school had a classroom equipped with chisels, spokeshaves, fretsaws and even more exotic tools. I still remember the teacher's sad voice when he told me I would have to drop technical drawing and study Latin. The appropriate comment, *eheu fugaces*, didn't occur to either of us.

The 1960s

Free love and sit-ins were compulsory for the arts faculty but we medics plodded respectably from school to graduation. Planeloads of us went to North America for our summer elective, which was why I saw pictures of the 1969 moon landing live in Toronto. The weather was hot and I was beginning to wonder if this free love thing might be worth a try. There were hospital parties but it remained elusive. Probably something to do with the dark jacket and shapeless trousers.

The 1970s

An obstetric career in those days began before graduation. The keen student could do instrumental deliveries and by the time I was a senior house officer, I was a dab hand at Kielland's rotation in the delivery room. A trial of forceps in theatre was a rare event, which may explain my generation's tinge of exasperation at the way assisted delivery has become a three-act opera which ain't over until the fat lady is sectioned.

We got married and had children — normal deliveries, by the consultant who was my boss. In those days, obstetricians were allowed to conduct normal deliveries and trainees knew which consultant was their boss. Then came the MRCOG viva, an exercise in mind-reading, as two elderly Fellows discussed unusual cases and you had to guess what they were thinking. If you were lucky, they disagreed with each other and started arguing.

All those learning experiences! Your first drug administration error. Your first fatally misinterpreted CTG. Your first maternal death. And all this without a logbook for reflective comments. You thought a lot, though, without having to tick a box to prove it. And then at last, the joy of crossing the divide into a senior registrar post. How soon before that barrier is reintroduced into training, I wonder?

The 1980s

Some aspects of the eighties seem modern. This was when I first saw a colleague with an ultrasound scanner in the antenatal clinic, smiling smugly because he knew which way up babies were while the rest of us were still guessing. But other aspects seem prehistoric. Evenings in the library, prowling the shelves with a list of references and spraining your wrist retrieving heavy volumes from the shelves. We academics developed an ability to photocopy at amazing speed, like surgeons operating in the pre-anaesthetic era. Sometimes we would even read the paper after photocopying it.

The 1990s

As we moved to conducting literature searches on the web, we began to believe that science had only just been invented. Few journals have digitised their pre-1995 archives, so we older authors have begun recycling our early papers. If I told you this article was first written in 1981 you wouldn't believe it, would you?

Doctor in the stalls

We spent yesterday evening at our local playhouse watching Lenny Henry in *Othello*. Naturally I don't want to give away the ending but I would advise you to bring some tissues. During the curtain calls the Leeds audience relieved its feelings by booing Iago. What a rotter! The company, Northern Broadsides, brings Shakespeare to life by using local accents and brilliant stagecraft, and this production sold out even before it got its rave reviews in the national press. Nevertheless as we looked around the packed 750-seat amphitheatre we recognised only one other doctor.

The reason most medics prefer concerts and opera for their evenings out is that we get quite enough drama during the daytime. Tragedy, comedy, pathos and conflict come and go through the clinic doors in an endless stream and when we finally get a break we head for the bar, like playgoers everywhere. These days, thanks to the recession, escapism is making a bit of a comeback but for years the main offering from British theatres was gritty social realism. That's the last thing we want on our night off.

Gorilla surprise

Nevertheless my wife and I (I think I speak for both of us, dear) like nothing better than settling down in comfy stalls on a Saturday night. Within minutes we're fast asleep. By the time we wake with a start and a guilty feeling, the action is well under way and having read the programme beforehand we can usually catch up and enjoy the really good bits. Sometimes, though, it's all over, particularly if I go alone. I regret to say I have slept with some of the most famous names in the West End and I think some of them noticed.

It wasn't always like that. As a student I was a habitué of the gallery (in 1964 I saw Olivier's Othello—not a patch on Lenny Henry's) and stayed alert, usually because I was infatuated with an actress. There was an especially pretty one in repertory in Cardiff, where I had a holiday job, and I went to every play in the series. The last one was set in a jungle and I sat through it, heart fluttering, but didn't see her—not until the end when the gorilla took a bow and removed its head. Happy days of youth, when I wasn't worn out by work. Perhaps I shall be less sleepy when I retire.

Move over, Will

Speaking of which, I have been nursing a vague ambition to become a playwright when I leave medicine and now the reality is looming. By the time you read this my retirement party will have come and gone and I may well be staring at a blank computer screen and hoping for inspiration. The advice in *Playwrighting for Dummies* is 'write what you know', which means my options are limited. Unless I can set a gripping drama on the train to London (Murder on the National Express, perhaps?), I shall be restricted to scripts about obstetrics and gynaecology.

Not a very inspiring prospect, you may think. Who would want to spend an evening listening to female characters reciting monologues about their vaginas? Or can you imagine a show called Women on the Verge of HRT? After a bit of research, however, I have discovered that this is exactly the stuff that is pulling in the punters (or punteuses) all around the country. So I'm already jotting down preliminary ideas:

- *Don't Push Now!*—a farce. Set in a labour ward where the doors keep flying open as one midwife tries to look after three patients, none of whom speaks English, while hiding a doctor who is trying to comply with the European Working Time Directive.
- *Once More unto the Breach*—a thriller. With the minutes ticking away, the clinical director desperately tries to deliver appointments to the last six outpatients. Will he meet Trust targets and prevent the hospital being closed forever?
- *M*R*S*A*—a sex comedy. How much of the doctor's clothing will the manager dare to remove on the ridiculous pretext of trying to reduce hospital infection rates?
- *Twelve Angry Men*—a mystery. Who has stolen the magazines from the locked room in the assisted conception unit?

Actually, that last title has already been taken, but you get the idea. See you on opening night, darlings.

What are you reading?

When I retired, two months ago, my intention was to spend part of each day curled up with a good book. Or perhaps stretched out, which may be healthier at my age. OK, I could work on the reading position but finding the book would be no problem. Our house is full of them, from the *Mr Men* series to the *Encyclopaedia Britannica*. (Our children left home years ago but I don't like throwing books out.) I was going to start with something between those extremes, though probably nearer the Roger Hargreaves end of the spectrum.

It's not been as easy as I thought. To be honest, I couldn't get motivated. As a boy I was a bookworm, sure, but then I went to university. That meant textbook after textbook, undergraduate then postgraduate. (It must be worse for today's membership candidates, struggling through shedloads of guidelines, most of which have no pictures at all.) Then I became a medical academic, reading po-faced reports with numbered paragraphs and bullet points, scanning NHS bumph full of words like 'overarching' and 'stakeholder' and editing papers in which the speling and, punctuition had to be scene two be believed. After a lifetime of professional reading, did I really want to do it for pleasure?

Don't laugh

I'm spoilt for choice and that's another problem. Some of the best reading experiences are when you're stuck in a lonely residency with no television and a small shelf of books placed there some time in the 1930s. Bored, you pick one up and discover just how good Charles Dickens or Mark Twain were. Or you're amazed to find that in the first half of the 20th century, authors could be funny. The golden age of humorous writing was when times were tough and readers wanted laughter without malice.

Today, bookshops are as big as supermarkets but the 'humour' section is tiny—a few picture books, something with swear words in the title and *Best Essex Girl Jokes Volume 3*. They don't have a section labelled 'Misery' but if they did, it would take up most of the ground floor. Memoirs of child abuse, confessions from celebrity rehab and detailed accounts of World War II go down big with the British public. Not to mention sprawling sagas of love, hardship and domestic violence spanning four generations.

Gender and elves

My wife gets to hear about novels that are actually interesting but that's because she belongs to a book group. I think (I'm on dangerous ground here, as a believer in gender equality) that women are better than men at this sort of thing. They can do networking without competing. But I can't believe they're so fickle, flitting from Azar Nafisi to Orlando Figes to A S Byatt without a backward glance. Men, by contrast, are serial monogamists—once we've read everything by our favourite author we grieve for a while, drink a little too much and turn to crosswords. After P G Wodehouse died I formed a long-term relationship with Evelyn Waugh but when he ran out on me I became celibate.

A lot of men (and women) enjoy fantasy. Not me, unfortunately. I just can't see the point of Discworld, hobbits or Lord Voldemort's Death Eaters. That makes me strange, I know. In fact, you may be beginning to wonder if I really exist. I wasn't always in the minority. At school one of my classmates was a Tolkien fan and the rest of us used to exchange knowing looks and tap our foreheads. Now, I imagine, any adolescent who doesn't believe in Frodo Baggins is likely to be offered counselling. We've seen him with our own eyes on the silver screen, haven't we? He lives in New Zealand.

Michael—at last

So you can see why the conversation opener, 'What are you reading?' (still sometimes heard at College dinners) makes me nervous. And you can understand why nothing came of the suggestion, years ago, that the Part 1 MRCOG should include a literary question—nobody would have been able to mark it. But all is not lost. On a plane recently I read *Headlong* by Michael Frayn. He wrote *Noises Off,* one of the funniest plays ever, and I hoped that once we reached cruising altitude I would fall off my seat laughing. Halfway through the book I realised it was more sophisticated than that but never mind, I was hooked. I've found Mr Intelligent and I hope we'll be happy together.

Have gadgets, will travel

I'm sitting in a hotel room in Central Asia, contemplating my memory stick. How times have changed. Twenty years ago this region was part of a communist empire, out of bounds to everyone west of Leningrad. Now the only memento of the Soviet Union is the code ('SU') of the Aeroflot flight that brought me here via Moscow. (A Boeing, very punctual.) Our workshop on confidential enquiries starts tomorrow but today is a national holiday and nothing is happening except displays of folk-dancing in the square outside. I can hear it from here. These days folk-dancing involves banks of loudspeakers and kiddies who know how to belt out a number through a radio mike.

The television in the room is multilingual with 24 channels. BBC World becomes slightly repetitive after the first few hours but Japan and Korea also broadcast rolling news programmes in English. They seem strange to UK eyes because the interviewers are respectful. Mixed with the news are items enticing tourists to visit but you have to wait until you hear the name 'Seoul' before you know which half of Korea they mean. Ho-hum. Enough of Michael Jackson's funeral. Time to call home. One button to press and there's my wife, alarmed, asking why I've woken her up.

How do they do that?

High technology, now so essential to life, is beyond my understanding. All those particles whizzing between my mobile and Leeds. At school, physics was a scary science associated with atom bombs and space travel. Now it's as user-friendly as a favourite sweater and we're lost without it. In fact, I'm feeling quite aggrieved that the hotel Wi-Fi doesn't reach this room. I shall have to take my laptop downstairs to read my email. A day without logging on? Perish the thought.

Looking at my USB stick, what upsets me is that I've no idea how it works. How can a bit of plastic with wires in it hold every lecture I've given since PowerPoint was invented? Not knowing is an unpleasant sensation. It makes you feel like a patient. The trouble is, you get used to it. iPods, plasma screens ... even a gadget on my key-ring that can open the garage door while still in my trouser pocket (thank goodness our family is complete). There ought to be a series of picture books *(Simply for the Over-60s)* explaining these things in big print for people like me.

Boys (and girls) with toys

But maybe a need to know is a gender thing. My wife doesn't share my primordial urge to take an MP3 player to pieces and find out how it works. Since the dawn of time it has been the male of the species who has dismantled the motorbike and spread the bits over the kitchen floor. So it's interesting that at this stage in the evolution of medicine, feminisation has coincided with the profession's increasing dependence on expensive gadgetry.

Already diagnosis rarely occurs without imaging—which, may I add, has been made difficult for generalists to do personally as the on/off switch is hidden in a different place on each scanner. Soon all invasive treatments will be performed by robots named after iconic renaissance men (a clever marketing touch, that), enabling doctors to avoid meeting patients altogether. These trends are often labelled 'boys with toys' (people love gender-based insults, especially if they rhyme) but actually women cope better with technology. They don't fiddle with it. Personally I detested complex apparatus that came between me and the patient. I preferred talking to her about her problem, an approach that managers regarded as embarrassingly quaint.

Grey power

Technophobia is generally perceived as being age related, like hair colour. I used to play up to this stereotype and call for help from young SpRs whenever I had a problem with a PC. Now that I'm retired, I've grown up. I can crawl under my own desk now, thank you. And listen to this. Last week I sorted out my wife's crashed internet connection. Please, no applause. It's just a matter of having the right attitude and, of course, the time. With no NHS targets to meet, you rediscover the ability to think and do things properly. Mind you, I mustn't speak too soon. I still have to go downstairs and transmit this article to Regent's Park. Wish me luck.

Lust in the upper circle

Pop stars aren't normally my thing but in the last week I've seen no fewer than two of them. First I noticed my wife eying a poster for a David Essex concert and I gallantly insisted on buying us tickets. He and I are the same age and he shot to stardom around the time I graduated, so we have something in common. Where we differ is that during the 1970s he kept being mobbed by hysterical female fans, whereas I spent my evenings in the medical library. Not that I'm jealous, you understand.

At 62, he still has enough sexual charisma to create a frisson in the upper circle. When I say 'frisson' I mean excited giggles among ladies of a certain age in the row behind us and explicit suggestions shouted by a less inhibited devotee nearer the front. It became clear that he was not going to remove his clothing as requested but nevertheless he responded appropriately. He gave our section of the audience a knowing look and the economical wiggle of a man who has been there, done that, and is now conserving his strength.

Gosh, I thought. This is a far cry from my days in the psychosex clinic. What a pleasant change to be among mature women who are in touch with their id, as Freud would have put it. Mind you, I couldn't help reflecting that the object of their desire was at a safe distance, protected by sinewy guitarists and a percussionist who, like all good drummers, spent much of the performance in a trance.

Pastilles, anyone?

The usual Saturday night gig for the Drifes is an orchestral concert, where rapture is more muted, though just as intense in its own way. A classical soloist in Leeds Town Hall does not have to cope with wolf-whistles, but the sound of a satisfied audience applauding with its feet as well as its hands is equally impressive. And there's an extra element of suspense because you don't know how the listeners feel until the very end (and, for some of us, because we don't know that it is the end until someone breaks the silence by clapping).

When I say 'silence' I use the term loosely. Quiet passages in a classical concert are reminiscent of the waiting room in the chest clinic but the coughing is actually psychological. Someone in the gallery gets bored and clears their throat, triggering an answering call from the stalls. Like birdsong, kindred spirits around the hall decide to mark their territory before the next fortissimo passage arrives. At least mobile phones are rarely heard, which is just as well. With so many ringtones now being melodies by Mozart, the conductor could get confused.

When the fat lady sings

The sex appeal of classical music is subtle in the extreme unless you include the programme notes, which tend to dwell on the composers' love lives. Musical creativity, even more than painting, is closely linked to the libido and apparently many a good tune is the result of unfulfilled desire. Though fulfilment can be just as stimulating. JS Bach had twenty children, all of whom had to be fed.

Where classical fervour becomes explicit is in opera. The standard plot (boy meets girl, boy loses girl, neither seeks professional help, one or both die a lingering death) is full of passion which can leave the heart and the mind deeply moved. But not the loins. Too often the soprano is bigger than the tenor and the only way she can beat her fists on his manly chest is if she kneels down.

Scrooge in Bradford

And the other pop star? Ah, now you're asking. It was someone who topped the charts when I was at school. His first record, in 1956, was *"Rock with the Caveman"* and he was touted as Britain's answer to Elvis. Sex symbols, however, need an air of danger and Tommy Steele (for it was he) comes across as a nice guy. He quickly became a family entertainer and last week he brought Dickens' *A Christmas Carol* to Bradfordians of all ages. Again the only seats left were in the upper circle but even at that range his charm embraced us easily. I loved it but I'm pretty sure my wife preferred David Essex. She still hasn't let go of his souvenir programme.

Editors of the Caribbean

I'm on my way to an editorial board meeting in Puerto Rico, a faraway country of which I know little. I recall that in *West Side Story* the Sharks were Puerto Rican, but today it's the real deal and I'm heading not for New York but for the Caribbean, a name that conjures up romance, adventure, pirates and Johnny Depp. Clearly this is no ordinary board meeting. I'm hoping for an editor in chief with a parrot on his shoulder, a statistician with an eye patch and a publisher hopping about on a crutch singing, 'Yo ho ho and a bottle of rum!' Will I get the Black Spot, I wonder?

Let me quickly say that it's nothing to do with this journal. The *TOG* editorial board, I imagine, meets in a spartan office in the College, or perhaps, conscious of its carbon footprint, it holds virtual meetings only. (I can't cope with those. I recently bought a webcam to communicate with our distant daughter. Her first question was, 'Why are you upside down?') No, this is an American journal which, wisely in my opinion, wants someone on the board to represent the rest of the world. Apparently Puerto Rico is part of the USA—at least in the same sense that Scotland is part of England.

Pans, Goons and Klim

American planes are bilingual these days, with signs in English and Spanish. I don't remember those from my last trip to the Caribbean. Mind you, that was in 1969 when I was a student, so I hardly qualify for frequent flyer status. After an undergraduate clerkship in Toronto I took a bus to Miami and a flight to Trinidad to chill out with fellow students whose parents lived there. ('Hi, remember me? I just happened to be passing ...') My friends were members of the Edinburgh Steel Band, Trinidad being the home of pan music. One of the great discoveries of my life at university was the exhilarating sound of tuned 55-gallon oil drums. Sadly, those musicians have gone their separate ways and Edinburgh has reverted to bagpipes.

In the 1960s Trinidad felt frightfully British, though warmer of course, so my 'chilling out' was purely metaphorical. The cricket ground was down the road and a local radio station broadcast *The Goon Show* in the afternoons. The programmes were interrupted by commercials, including one for powdered milk in which the jingle went, 'Klim is best for my baby!' and a voiceover added confidentially, 'Spell it backwards'. The British had taken over Trinidad from Spain in 1802. Puerto Rico, by contrast, had an impregnable fort and stayed Spanish until 1898, when the US arrived. It's just as well that it fell to the Americans rather than us Brits. *West Brom Story* wouldn't have been nearly as exciting.

OB and GYN in Puerto Rico

Puerto Rico's fame in our specialty rests on the fact that it was where the first clinical trial of the oral contraceptive pill was carried out, way back in 1956. I had always felt uneasy about this, thinking it was an early example of scientific colonialism, but it turns out that this was where the manufacturers were based and, indeed, another trial in California began a few months later. Today pharmaceuticals represent 25% of Puerto Rico's gross domestic product and 60% of its exported commodities. Rio Piedras, where the pill trial was conducted, is home to the University of Puerto Rico's main campus. The town's population more than doubled between 1950 and 1980, so maybe they concentrated a bit too much on the export market.

Today what interests epidemiologists is the country's rising caesarean section rate. In 2007 it reached 49%, compared with an overall US rate of 32% (ranging from 22% in Utah to 38% in New Jersey) but Puerto Rican women who migrate to the mainland have the same rate as local women. As I check these figures it's easy to get sidetracked. I see that low birthweight in American Samoa is only 3.3% (which sounds like an argument for localised charts) and that by far the highest rate of births to unmarried mothers (71.5%) is in the Virgin Islands.

Vuelve pronto

On my way home now, with just enough space to report that the meeting was excellent and the air-conditioning worked well. We were the only hotel guests not wearing shorts and there wasn't a parrot in sight.

Westering home

I've just returned from my second trip to the Outer Hebrides. The first was 16 years ago, when I flew there to give a lecture. I still blush at the memory of my accurate but massive expenses claim (you have to change planes at Glasgow and stay overnight in Stornoway) for a talk on some academic topic irrelevant to clinical practice on a small island. The long-suffering audience consisted of local doctors. I noticed that many of them hailed originally from southern England but had evidently decided to settle as far away from the Thames Estuary as possible.

The distance from London to Stornoway is, in fact, the same as from London to Bayreuth or Zermatt, but it feels a lot further. There are no opera-houses or ski runs on the Western Isles, which is why some people like the place so much. My second visit was purely for pleasure and this time my wife and I arrived by sea, like the Celts and Norsemen once did. Well, not exactly. Our ferry had been converted for upmarket cruising, with a captain and chefs from Glasgow and waiters from Eastern Europe, all of them charming. Eric the Viking, eat your heart out.

History lessons

A couple of millennia ago the outer isles were on a busy sea route, along which trade continued into the Middle Ages. You can still clamber around Iron Age brochs but the famous Lewis chessmen, lost by a merchant and buried for 600 years, have been taken to Edinburgh or the British Museum. Just as well, otherwise they might not have inspired the creation of that epic cartoon, Noggin the Nog. More recently the isles' principal export was people, mainly to Australasia and North America, where many of them became business leaders and politicians. Few got as far as South America, which is a pity. They might have established stable democracies there too, though whether Scots blood would have improved the football is debatable.

The most poignant depopulation was of the small archipelago of St Kilda, forty miles west in the Atlantic. In the 19th century its population fell steadily until the last three dozen people requested evacuation in 1930. I had always felt some professional guilt about this because I thought the main reason for the decline was that the babies died of tetanus after bird dung had been applied to the umbilicus. It turns out that the spores were everywhere and the high neonatal death rate was not, after all, due to a lack of evidence-based maternity care. I could hold my obstetric head high.

Song and story

When we reached Tobermory—now, apparently, familiar to a new generation of television viewers as *'Balamory'*—we headed for the local video shop. In the late 1940s the British film industry had a brief love affair with the Western Isles and those classic DVDs are even more fun if you are looking out for familiar places as well as enjoying the English stars' valiant attempts at the accent. *Whisky Galore!* was based on the true story of the wreck of a ship loaded with Scotland's best-loved product. Bottles retrieved by the locals and hidden from the customs men were still being found in rabbit holes years later. It was filmed partly on the remote island of Barra. The main street is easily recognisable, though one of the houses is now the Café Kisimul, specialising in Indian cuisine (and highly recommended).

For a lowland Scot like myself, all this was a foreign country which nonetheless felt strangely familiar. At school we were taught Hebridean songs, translated from Gaelic and named after romantic-sounding islands like Eriskay and Mingulay. They had been passed down by oral tradition and collected by Marjory Kennedy Fraser, a folklorist who started life as a music-hall artiste. When I was a boy no Christmas pantomime was complete without a sing-song mingling these with modern imitations like 'Westering Home', written by a city choirmaster about the rigours of crossing the ocean under sail. Moist-eyed Glasgow theatre-goers, many of them of Hebridean stock, sang them all with equal wistfulness.

Pass the binoculars, dear

My wife has just pointed out that I have said nothing about the sea birds, the grey seals, the dolphins or the golden eagle. They moved too quickly for me. Nor have I mentioned the Harris tweed, but when I wear it to Regent's Park I think you'll be impressed.

Becoming a consultant

Our daughter recently became a consultant. Children grow up so quickly these days. One minute they are being kitted out with their first school uniform; the next they are on the specialist register. When I was her age I was still a trainee. Things are different, I know, in her non-surgical specialty, but becoming the father of a consultant is always a major life event. I may need counselling. Meanwhile, please bear with me while I go misty-eyed and nostalgic, recalling my own early faltering consultant steps all those years ago.

But first, to find out whether things have changed since 1982, I googled the title of this article. It was a chilling reality check. There are thousands of websites aimed at non-doctors, explaining how much to charge, how to work from home and how to persuade big organisations (like the NHS) to hire lay advisors. No experience necessary. One site, however, does provide a Department of Health information pack. It tells medical trainees what they will need to know as consultants (for example, how to construct a business case) and includes three pages of tick boxes. Welcome to your new job.

When I were a lad ...

In the 1970s junior doctors saw the same consultants day after day, observed them intently and knew more about their funny little ways than they knew themselves. As your training progressed, you became increasingly adept at predicting the boss's reaction to any of life's challenges and, ultimately, at manipulating it. Senior registrars could amuse the doctors' mess with devastatingly accurate mimicry. Your career progression depended on knowing each chief and ensuring that the right management option was implemented on the right day of the week, depending on which consultant was on call.

One of the shocks of becoming a consultant was realising that you had to make up your own mind about what to do. Your practice quickly gelled into an amalgam of the best bits of what you'd seen during training. This Darwinian evolution of medicine and surgery has come to a halt now, as neither trainees nor consultants dare to stray beyond College guidelines.

I feel guilty about this stifling of progress because I played my part in it. Soon after becoming a consultant I helped to produce a labour ward protocol which unified practice among the various obstetricians in our hospital. I still have a copy of the booklet—a few A5-size pages with short notes. The rest of the information was kept in your head. Well, yours and the registrar's. Well, OK, mainly the registrar's.

What not to wear

Top hats for doctors went out of fashion before I entered medicine, though some senior nurses still mourned their passing. The bowler hat was stylish in the 1960s but soon became the uniform of judges in agricultural shows. As consultanthood approached, I gave some thought to creating the right impression and on my first day I turned up wearing a trilby and a large raincoat. I now realise that I looked like Humphrey Bogart in search of the Maltese Falcon. I still remember the expression on a colleague's face as he peered under the brim and exclaimed, 'Gosh, it's Jim!'

In those days, consultant style simply meant trying to avoid looking as if you had dressed in a hurry with the light off. Nowadays young men spend a lot of money trying to achieve just that look. Government ministers appear on television without a tie and even weather forecasters, heaven help us, are letting their standards drop, at least on cable channels. What is a chap to do? No wonder our specialty has undergone feminisation. There is no dress code for men.

Discovering the real you

Watching generations of trainees metamorphose into consultants, I've found it hard to predict which type of butterfly would emerge from which chrysalis. Sometimes a passionate interest in research would die overnight. Sometimes an outspoken rebel would become an effective clinical director. Sometimes a workaholic would turn to house building or smallholding. Most mystifying of all were the trainees who seemed to become instantly wealthy.

Usually, however, caring SpRs turn into caring consultants. The transition is less scary than it was. My daughter has an official mentor, whereas in my day the arrangement was informal. I remember with gratitude the senior consultant who murmured, 'If you need any help, call me'. We're still in touch, only now it's by email.

Old school ties

Going back to your old school is an unfamiliar experience. Alumni who win an Olympic gold medal or *The X Factor* are likely to be asked back, but for the rest of us the Alma Mater remains un-revisited. Certainly that's how it was for me until a few weeks ago, when I attended a class reunion which involved strolling down the old familiar corridors. It was an educational experience and deserves a spot in *TOG*.

That school was the last of four that I attended before university. We lived in the country, in a place called Muirkirk, which meant I moved from one village school to another before finally taking the bus to an academy in the nearest town. The daily commute was a godsend as you got an extra half hour to finish your homework. You had to write as the bus was pulling away from each stop, before your handwriting became too shaky.

The class of 1959

The academy's class of '59 was already well established when I joined in '61. My arrival gave the Latin teacher an opportunity for humour. Our set author, Julius Caesar, had a low opinion of his opponents, the barbarians. When we reached his descriptions of their hovels and unhygienic habits, the teacher would say, 'Just like Muirkirk, eh, Drife?' Cue laughter, even from me. I appreciated his comic timing and rather liked the idea of being perceived as a woad-covered Celt.

Fifty years on, my Latin is a bit rusty. Indeed, until last month I would have said I remember almost nothing of my schooldays. Yes, there was my teenage crush on the prettiest girl in the bus. And the term when I was banished to the back of the chemistry laboratory after my fountain pen exploded. And, of course, the magic moment when our chess team won the county league. But otherwise, a blank.

The reunion

Organising a reunion is easy nowadays, thanks to the internet, but only if someone is willing to put in the work. Gavin, the classmate who volunteered, did us proud, even coaxing us to write mini-autobiographies for a souvenir booklet. Not everyone turned up, and a disconcerting number had gone to the great classroom in the sky. I knew that being Scottish was bad for your health but I was shaken to witness epidemiology at first hand. The bar bill for us survivors was modest, though some did nip out for a smoke.

We spent the whole weekend smiling. Our shared roots made conversation easy, and retirement removed any sense of competition. Besides, that list of obituaries put things into perspective. We talked about our children and agreed that they all lived on another planet. Grandkids, however, kindled real enthusiasm. My classmates had criss-crossed the globe but most still lived in Scotland, despite the health risks, and one was now a stalwart of the national chess championships.

Better late than never

So where did the education come in? Well, I learned about my home town. It now has a museum of the mining industry, once the lifeblood of the area. I knew nothing about working underground except for an appalling memory from the age of ten, when seventeen men from our village, including a classmate's dad, died in an explosion. The museum illustrated details about the hewing of coal and gave it a romantic glow, but I wasn't fooled. The pits are gone, and good riddance.

The next lesson was how easily schools can become neglected. The building that had transformed our lives had not prospered. True, there was a roomful of computers, but the exterior had seen hardly a lick of paint since the 1960s, or so it seemed. As we walked around we focused on our memories and avoided taking too critical a look at what our generation was handing on to the next but one.

And there was that souvenir booklet. It was a revelation. My classmates' self-penned histories were stunningly honest and I realised I had hardly known them. Gavin, for example, left school early because his miner dad was going blind. Starting as an apprentice in electronics, Gavin became an international expert on semiconductors, working for a corporation involved in mobile communications. He must have helped kick-start the revolution in social networking that occupies so much of our kids' time on that other planet. Good for him. If our class had had iPhones, we might not have taken so long to start talking.

On line in the attic

When I worked in hospital, my office had a panoramic view of the roof of the outpatient department. Now that I'm retired, my study overlooks a golf course. Prettier, yes, but I have to climb onto my desk to see it. The attic is a good place to work if you don't mind seasonal variations in temperature and a sprint down two flights whenever the doorbell rings. It's quiet up here, and the high window means I'm less likely to be distracted from my computer screen.

Not now, Nora, I'm editing

Retirement in Yorkshire. It conjures up images from Last of the Summer Wine — outdoor strolls and mischief with Nora Batty. In reality, we bus pass holders sit hunched over our keyboards, emailing complaints to the head of BBC Radio and trying to compensate for our memory lapses. (If you start to type the question 'Where are my slippers?' Google completes it for you.) And we discover Amazon, which is why the doorbell keeps ringing.

But there's still work to be done. My attic is a publishing nerve-centre, with papers flowing to the *European Journal of Obstetrics & Gynecology and Reproductive Biology* from every continent except (as yet) Antarctica. If authors are far away, so are my editorial colleagues. The journal office is in Amsterdam, the manager is in Shannon, the typesetters are somewhere in Asia and other editors are dotted across the globe from Glasgow to Hong Kong. We grumble about the quirks of the electronic system that binds us together but it's a big improvement on the days when manuscripts arrived in torn brown envelopes. I miss the stamps, though.

Of course, I'm not unique. There are now 5516 journals listed in the catalogue of the US National Library of Medicine, and I imagine about 5500 of them are edited either in attics or by working doctors in moments snatched between clinics. Medical editing is a cottage industry, reminiscent of handloom weaving in Yorkshire before the dawn of mechanisation. We pass our finely crafted material to t' gaffer (a giant publishing corporation which owns several hundred other titles) and we are rewarded by an annual works outing. It's a reet good day out, is Amsterdam.

Your password is not recognised

Editors sometimes review papers for one another. Whenever I do this I'm amazed, occasionally at the brilliance of the science, but always at how the process has changed over the years. When I was a senior lecturer, the conscientious referee had to visit a library, leaf through Index Medicus, dash around collecting bound journals and learn how to use the photocopier. It took a great deal of hard physical work to discover that a paper under review had already been published somewhere else.

Now, I can do it in a jiffy — well, OK, rather a long jiffy — without leaving the attic. Seeing familiar journals online is like meeting old friends on Facebook, except that finding them is much harder. You have to click on 'Library', which is in tiny font at the foot of my university's homepage and well hidden in the RCOG website. Modern organisations seem embarrassed at having something so old-fashioned in an era of processed information. And rather like the Middle Ages, when libraries chained books to the shelves, everything important is password protected. Have you ever tried to access the full text of a Cochrane review?

Still, it's worth persisting. My biggest thrill is searching journals that have put their entire content online. *The New England Journal of Medicine* goes back to 1 January 1812, when the very first paragraph pointed out that 'a knowledge of preceding discoveries' is essential to inquiry into any medical subject. Try telling that to most medical journals, whose online content starts around 1995. An honourable exception is *BJOG*, whose first paragraph, in 1902, reminds us that it was started long before the foundation of the RCOG.

You rotten swine, you!

Sadly, my way of life in the attic is now under threat. I have discovered Radio 7. Launched in 2002 to broadcast the BBC sound archive, it is available on my computer and harks back to my schooldays, the golden age of wireless. Some programmes I can resist but when Tony Hancock or the Goons are on, everything has to stop. I even swither about Paul Temple. How I regret those emails to the head of BBC Radio. This is her revenge.

Land of my mothers

The Drife family takes its name from a river in Scotland. Quite a short one, but at least it gives us a geographical identity. My surname, though, is only part of my heritage. My mitochondrial DNA and 50% of my genes come from the female line, which is forced to remain anonymous. It has always struck me as sexist that a woman's name changes when she marries. She could insist on hyphenation, perhaps, but this becomes impractical after three or four generations, when your notepaper has to be turned sideways to accommodate your signature.

My mother's maiden name was Jones. Yes, there is a Jones River, which is even shorter than the Water of Dryfe. It is somewhere in Massachusetts and was named after the captain of the *Mayflower*. If we are related, it must be distantly. Jones is the fourth most common surname in the USA and the second most common in Britain. There are almost 400,000 of them (or should I say 'us') here, with the highest concentration in North Wales. Mum would be disappointed to hear that. She was a South Wales girl and regarded the north as an alien land where people mispronounce Welsh by talking through their noses.

It's a boy, bach

I was introduced to the Welsh language early in life, when we returned to my mother's roots every year for our summer holidays. Come to think of it, I may have had my first lesson in utero, as I was born in Cardiff with the help of a Welsh-speaking midwife. Labour lasted 27 hours (I was told later), which would have been long enough to reach 'Plural of nouns and adjectives' if they had worked systematically through *Teach Yourself Welsh*. More likely they stuck to the conversational method, but it didn't work for me. I've just looked up the word for 'push' ('gwthio') and it rang no bells. Mind you, after a 27-hour labour it's probably just as well that I don't remember Mum's exact words.

A few weeks later in Scotland I was shown to my dad and began retuning my ears to English. Then I settled into a pattern of annual transcultural migration that must be familiar to many doctors, though in my case it did not involve intercontinental flights but steam trains to Newport, Gwent and points west. Every summer my accent changed twice. I was taken to chapel and eventually the Welsh hymn-book held no terrors for me, though I didn't know what I was singing. My fondest memories are of the seaside, where I met aged relatives with smiling eyes and a limited English vocabulary.

Tenors galore

Like many couples of their generation, my parents had met during the Second World War. In battle-scarred Italy, a wounded soldier was treated by a cheerful physio and love blossomed. I used to think their shared Celtic background must have had a lot to do with it, but actually Scotland and Wales have little in common. Today each country has its own parliament, runs its own health service and loudly asserts its non-Englishness, but otherwise they are very different. Take music, for example. Scotland's traditional instrument, the bagpipes, is a military weapon, while Wales is the land of the male voice choir. When Welshmen sing, they revel in pure sound – a trait they share with Russians and Zulus. Explain that, geneticists.

These days it's the music that keeps drawing me back. I have yet to see Tom Jones (another relative?) in concert but we like to visit Cardiff's magnificent new opera-house, officially called the 'Millennium Centre'– or, better,'Canolfan Mileniwm', which sounds less like a shopping mall. Even better than Verdi with Welsh surtitles, however, are occasional musical surprises, such as when I was among a group of gynaecologists visiting Swansea. When our bus reached the hotel, we saw that our host had filled the foyer and staircase with a huge choir of men from the valleys, in matching blazers. The sound was stunning. Thank goodness they weren't bagpipers.

Diolch a nosda

Now that Scotland is thinking of seceding from the Union, I am getting in touch with my Welsh side. I have bought a new *Teach Yourself* book and thanks to cable television I can watch an ethnic soap opera, set in North Wales but not noticeably nasal. Already, as you see, I can say thank you and goodnight.

Getting out

One of the drawbacks about working in hospital is that you are indoors all the time. It wasn't always like this. I can remember when patients were wheeled outside for a bit of sunshine and when wards in smaller hospitals were linked by paths rather than corridors. Florence Nightingale (before my time) was keen on fresh air but her influence on hospital design was waning when I qualified. By then, architects were designing operating theatres without windows and placing gynaecology outpatient clinics in the basement. As a result, during my working life I rarely saw the sun. In Yorkshire in winter you arrived at work before dawn and it was dark again when you left. You only knew it was summer when patients turned up with pink shoulders. Ee, but try telling that to kids these days! They don't believe it.

When I retired I decided to get out more but I took it in easy stages. I began by watching a lot of television, which is full of programmes about the British countryside. They were a revelation. Presenters at various stages of pregnancy strode across magnificent scenery in all weathers while their non-pregnant colleagues assisted with difficult labours in the lambing shed. It looked as if any rural excursion might turn into a busman's holiday. How would I cope with ruptured membranes on the Pennine Way or locked twins in a Border Leicester?

What's my inside leg, dear?

Then I took a walk down Memory Lane. As a child in a Scottish village I was dragged from the wireless every Sunday afternoon for a hike across the heather. Today the moorland has signposted paths and the bus shelter has a map of memorials to Presbyterian martyrs shot for resisting King James and his bishops. Fifty-odd years ago, that part of Scotland felt like uncharted territory, and Dad and I would stumble across crumbling bits of national heritage almost by chance. At that age I found it boring, and my enforced marches left me sceptical about the benefits of healthy exercise.

Recently, however, browbeaten by epidemiologists, my wife and I have kitted ourselves out with boots, cagoules, woolly hats and those transparent map holders that you hang round your neck. We still get lost but we meet nice people, less articulate than those encountered by the television personalities but nonetheless happy to explain that our target pub is in the other direction and won't be open until Thursday. I marvel at my wife's in-depth knowledge of plants and birds but both of us are still a bit weak on butterflies. Being ambushed by the weather brings out the best in us. Soaked in Cornwall, we took refuge in a 13th century church where a sympathetic lady told us we had missed the last bus back to our hotel. Fair enough: it was nearly 4 p.m. On another occasion, inundated on Flamborough Head, we drove soggily to the nearest Marks & Spencer for sanctuary and dry trousers.

Art al fresco

Deep down, though, we're still aesthetes who enjoy nature mixed with art. The Yorkshire Sculpture Park is a big estate dotted with Henry Moore figures, enormous bits of welding and, last year, trees carved into abstract shapes by a sculptor wielding a two-man electric saw. The parkland itself receives regular maintenance and we are never quite sure whether chaps on tractors are creative artists or genuine coppicers. Either way, we gaze admiringly at their piles of twigs before heading uphill to the next totem pole.

We also like romantic ruins and there are plenty of those in Yorkshire. The Cistercians had their abbeys confiscated by Henry VIII, who removed, among other things, the lead from their roofs. Henry's Reformation owed more to his fertility problems than to religious fundamentalism, so it's no wonder those Scots preachers disliked it. Today, Fountains Abbey, deep in the dales and open to the elements, hosts occasional musical events. It may not look like a Parisian garret but its *La Bohéme,* with four singers and a piano, was unbearably moving. Last week Kirkstall Abbey, equally picturesque beneath the final approach to Leeds Bradford Airport, was doing Shakespeare. It was wonderful. We became utterly engrossed in the quarrels of Beatrice and Benedick, a few feet away across the grass. No lights, no microphones, just great acting. And this time it stayed dry.

Happy anniversary

Like most men, I've always had a blind spot for anniversaries. This year, however, I'm making an effort. I've checked out 2012, at least as far as January, and noted Joan of Arc's 600th birthday, Frederick the Great's 300th, Jackson Pollock's 100th and the centenaries of the African National Congress and the Republic of China. There is some danger of my losing the will to live before I get to February, with Charles Dickens' bicentennial and the Queen's diamond jubilee.

Discovering anniversaries used to be much more fun. During the tragically short life of the RCOG diary (2000–10) the tedious task of underlining my nights on call was enlivened by the tiny print at each date, recording a historic event. Each year they were different. Without those diaries I might never have known that my wife's birthday is the anniversary of the first slalom ski race in 1922 and the coronation of King Harold II in 1066. Or that we were married exactly 10 years after the first woman was launched into space.

The start of life

More significant for me than those giant leaps for humankind is my upcoming personal landmark: 40 years in obstetrics and gynaecology. Yes, I know. I can't believe it, either. But there it is on my CV: October 1972, my first job in the specialty. Actually, my hands-on experience had started long before that, because in the 1960s senior medical students were full members of the clinical team. We did locums, had our own cubicle in the antenatal clinic, and in the labour ward we could apply forceps — even rotational ones — under the registrar's watchful gaze (usually).

How scary it all was. I still remember my postgraduate anxiety when I realised I was about to repair the episiotomy of a lady whom I had stitched as an undergraduate after her first delivery. It was she who recognised me, of course, not the other way round, and I tried to look unsurprised that she had healed well enough to conceive again. In case you're wondering, in those days we did call women 'ladies', almost all deliveries involved a routine episiotomy, and suturing was not done by midwives. And in a small maternity unit it was not unusual for a doctor (or student) to see the same patient twice.

For better or worse

The four decades since then have seen many innovations: IVF, real-time ultrasound, urogynaecology, operative laparoscopy, etc, etc, and I'm tempted to reminisce at mind-numbing length about what life was like before them. In a word, it was awful. Facing infertile couples when you had nothing to offer, or starting a laparotomy with only a hunch about what you would find, are unhappy memories that are best avoided. Reviewing the results of a D&C for menorrhagia or an anterior repair for stress incontinence used to be exercises in self-delusion for both doctor and patient, as we tried to reassure each other that things were getting better. But at least doctors did see patients for review. The idea of undertaking follow-up by getting someone else to phone would have seemed like a dereliction of duty amounting almost to malpractice. We even had postnatal clinics (where the attendance rate was around 50%) and — get this — doctors did rounds in the postnatal wards, where women stayed for a week, learning to look after their babies. A bit OTT perhaps, but surely better than chucking them out after 6 hours, having made the wards so understaffed and overcrowded that they're glad to leave.

Forty years on

There I go. I can sense that your mind is starting to numb and I apologise. That's the trouble with anniversaries: you end up getting all nostalgic. I knew this would happen. I originally called this column *Forty Years On* but decided the heading might put you off. It's the name of a satirical play written by Alan Bennett in 1968, when our generation was sick and tired of hearing our elders reminiscing. I've just discovered that Bennett got the title from a song written in 1872 (hey — another anniversary!) to be sung regularly at a famous English public school, with the aim of giving the youngsters some inkling of how they will feel when they're ... well, my age. What a jolly good idea! Any chance of changing the headline back?

The King and I

Thanks in part to the Queen's diamond jubilee, memoirs of the 1950s are in vogue right now. If I'm going to join in, I should be quick before your appetite is sated. Indeed, I sense some scepticism already. We both know how inaccurate a patient's history can be, and you are probably bracing yourself for a fictional re-imagining of my early childhood. Well, let me reassure you. Although I was only four at the time, my earliest memory can be dated, precisely, to Wednesday, 6 February 1952. (OK, I had to check the day of the week.) We were living in a small town in Scotland. Suddenly, our neighbour, Mrs Stewart, began banging on our back door with the handle of a kitchen utensil. I can see her now, peering over the dividing wall. She said, 'The King's dead', and my mother burst into tears.

I didn't quite know how to cope. Naturally, I assumed that my mother and King George VI had been close, if not intimate, friends, but she explained between sobs that no, they had never met, don't be so silly James, go back and play with your toys. The mystery etched the moment onto my memory and it was only much later that I pieced things together. In the 1930s my mother, like all the girls, had had a crush on the charismatic King Edward VIII but during the War everyone grew to love the stammering George. Royals and commoners alike were losing members of their families and the King chose to take his chances amid the air raids alongside his fellow Londoners. None of them knew who would be next to die. Even now I don't think I can truly understand the bond this created.

During the War

That phrase, 'during the War', was used incessantly during the 50s and we children became heartily sick of it. After the First World War, survivors like my grandpa never spoke about their experiences, and we were all grateful to them for that. World War II was different. The entire population had, in a sense, been mobilised and of course they talked about it, though they glossed over the bad bits with euphemisms. My parents had met in Italy when the Allies were battling their bloody way northwards, and our house was still dotted with souvenirs – a sunny picture of Mount Vesuvius, a musical box that played 'Come Back to Sorrento', and some wonderful cartoons drawn by a German prisoner of war, showing wounded soldiers receiving physiotherapy from my mum in an atmosphere of general hilarity.

No wonder, then, that a military culture persisted all through the 1950s. My dad had briefly been a sergeant-major and our Sunday afternoon walks would begin with the instruction, 'You there, boy there! Chin-in-chest-out-shoulders-back-stomach-in. By the left, quick march!' Not that I took any notice. The standard haircut for men and boys was the army-style short back and sides, and our fathers must have regarded it as mutiny when The Beatles appeared with their tonsorial revolution. The officer classes (which included the medical profession) were automatically obeyed and their occasional ineptitude was accepted with good humour. Now do you see why I sometimes feel a bit wistful?

Call the midwife

I had few personal encounters with doctors at that time. Some of my contemporaries had childhood experiences as patients that inspired them to enter medicine, but not me. I have no recollection of the man who took my adenoids out, though I'm told he kick-started my academic career by enabling me to breathe through my nose and hear what the teacher was saying. I didn't meet any midwives until I was a student in the 1960s, when I was struck by their lack of nostalgia for the previous decade. Their attitude to the golden age of home delivery was rather like my grandpa's view of the trenches: they had seen horrible things and didn't want to talk about them.

It was all a long time ago and genuine memories get mixed up with the 'faction' of movies and television dramas. Even contemporary newsreels look staged. The best link to the reality of the 50s comes, paradoxically, on a digital radio channel, BBC Radio 4 Extra. You really understand people when you know what makes them laugh, and 60-year-old comedies like *The Goon Show* seem delightfully innocent. It's an odd adjective to apply to battle-hardened veterans but, yes, people were innocent in the 50s. It wasn't just me.

Up and at 'em

When you retire, you begin to calm down. It doesn't happen right away, and if you're already a very relaxed person it may not happen at all – though I suspect that even the most unflappable obstetrician gets wound up occasionally by life's little irritants, such as the NHS. Leaving these behind is a great relief, and it's ages now since I've been really annoyed about anything. Unless you count this new laptop, with its hypersensitive touch pad and insatiable desire to correct my sentence construction. For heaven's sake, Mr Office Assistant! I'll have you know I was writing English while you were still a twinkle in the eye of your foreign designer. Push off!! And take your helpful smile with you!

Anyway, as I was saying, nothing bothers me these days. I'm not sure that this is entirely a good thing. Getting a rush of blood to the head is a kind of reassurance that the life force is still present, even if it is followed by a deep sense of embarrassment. I used to blame it on my hormones. Aggression is supposed to be linked to testosterone, despite the fact that bad temper isn't restricted to males. When Mrs Thatcher was in Downing Street her office would issue regular press releases stating that 'the Prime Minister is furious' about something or other. The intention was to induce fear and trembling all around Westminster and especially among our European partners.

The rivals

Politicians know that passion plays well with the public and that every nation needs an enemy. The Scottish, Welsh and Irish gang up on the English. The English, in turn, have a long tradition of making unfunny jokes about the French – their nearest neighbours and therefore the natural target for stereotyping. The more I travelled, the more I realised that two nations rarely live harmoniously side by side. In the Far East, I was surprised that Siam and Burma used to have frequent wars. In Central Asia recently, our conference was relocated because of conflict between Uzbeks and Kyrgyz. Back home in the North of England, tribalism persists: Leeds United and Manchester United still wear the colours of the Wars of the Roses and their fans' mutual hatred is quite disturbing to outsiders.

Rivalry used to be a major driving force in medicine. Years ago London had a dozen hospital-based medical schools, each with its own rugby team, whose requirements, it's said, influenced the selection criteria for entry to the school. Winning on the pitch was a priority in the absence of any other indicators of academic excellence. Elsewhere in England, each town had two hospitals which did their best to ignore each other. If you worked in one, you never visited the other. Sometimes you got a phone call: the switchboard would say, 'Sorry, doctor, I have a message from the Dark Side', and your opposite number – someone you had never met – would tell you their neonatal unit was full and a case of triplets was already heading towards you. Naturally you assumed they were simply clearing the decks for another of their mess parties, which you had heard were the last word in debauchery.

All in a good cause

Things are different now that hospitals have coalesced into Trusts, with non-stop reshuffling of departments and rotation of employees. Overall this is an improvement, I suppose, but staff must find it a tad boring to have nobody to fight with. It's all very well getting together in superteams to battle disease and obesity, but such abstract or wobbly adversaries don't set many pulses racing. Most of us need tangible opponents, which is why hospital managers have such a hard time these days. In the past all the woes of St Wilfred's Hospital could be blamed on those rotters at St Mildred's across town. Now there is nobody to grumble about except the top management of the United All Saints University Hospital NHS Foundation Trust.

A few of my contemporaries still retain their youthful idealism and direct their fighting spirit against worthwhile foes, like creeping privatisation or world overpopulation. I take my hat off to them. My favourite role model is an elderly doctor I once met in Edinburgh. She had published the definitive studies of breast histology in 1934 and her papers were key references in my MD thesis. When I met her in the late 1980s she was still at her microscope, making notes. She briefly acknowledged my thanks before saying, 'Sorry, I have to get on'. For her, time was the enemy, and she wasn't going to be beaten.

Encyclopaedic knowledge

Our house is full of books, most of them written by great authors, some famous and some unknown (at least to me). My wife has read them all and I rely on her to come to my rescue when the conversation turns to literature at a posh dinner or an intellectual medical soiree. At home, my part of our shared (and still growing) library is upstairs – an old-fashioned world of classic detective stories and Wodehousean silliness. Whatever happened to lighthearted fiction, I wonder? Today, in bookshops the "humour" section consists of cartoons and Essex girl jokes, and in newspapers scholarly wit is restricted to the letters page and the cryptic crossword.

Although I rarely read novels now, I still have a weakness for reference books. Like many men, I read road atlases for pleasure, but I must admit that my real love is encyclopaedias. Ours are still downstairs, 32 volumes on a long shelf behind the television set. They are beautiful to look at but are rarely consulted in the internet era. Only when Google falls short do I politely ask Jeremy Paxman to budge up a bit so I can crawl past him and heave out the ultimate authority.

Looking at the pictures

My love affair with big books began early. It may be a genetic thing. My parents had kept their own childhood copies of *Cassell's Book of Knowledge* (a mere eight volumes) and I have them still. When first published in the 1920s they were a major advance: every page had a monochrome photograph or drawing, often of an historical figure or an exotically costumed foreigner. Today's reader is struck by the lack of ecological awareness (there are instructions on how to capture and kill a condor) and by their confidence in the Empire, with titles that evoke *Hello!* magazine. Canada is "The Land of the Maple Leaf – Britain's eldest daughter", and one caption is: "How Captain Cook was welcomed in Tasmania".

My parents, keen to advance my education, invested in a 1950s version, *Newnes Pictorial Knowledge*. It delighted me but now looks disturbingly similar to its predecessors. Its use of Victorian paintings gave a pre-Raphaelite tinge to history, and seven pages were devoted to TE Lawrence, "a great and gallant Englishman…who welded the Arabs together as no man had ever done before". I was more interested in the 14 pages on the 1953 ascent of Everest by Hillary and Tensing. Small boys need heroes and those books knew it.

Author! Author!

It never occurred to me to ask who wrote them. The authors, photographers and artists who influenced generations of children were anonymous and the editors, though named, are largely forgotten. Readers simply assumed that the text had been handed down from gods on Mount Olympus. Imagine my feelings, then, when late in my career I began to receive invitations to contribute to reference books. Summing up our specialty in seven pages for the *Oxford Companion to Medicine* was scary but providing an entry for the *Dictionary of National Biography (DNB)* was even more nerve-racking. Yes, the subject was dead and couldn't complain, but his family weren't and could. The *DNB* is rigorous and every fact must be double-checked, so the relatives were happy. We contributors were offered a discount: I fancied buying the 60 volumes (and a bookmark) but my wife said we did not have the necessary nine feet of shelf space.

My most recent effort, written several years ago, is an article on "Obstetrics" in the *Encyclopedia of Sciences and Religions*, which seems to be slanted towards the latter, as it is edited by professors of theology, one in Denmark and one in Spain. Its preparation has proceeded at an ecclesiastical pace but the publisher, Springer, says it will be appear in March 2013. Like the *DNB*, it presented authors with a structured series of questions, which included: "Is [your specialty] a science or a religion?" or "Please describe the belief systems which underlie [your specialty]". Perhaps I should have organised one of those annoying questionnaires to gauge the views of fellows and members but, full of the confidence of middle-age, I wrote the entry and my wife refereed it – favourably, I'm glad to say.

It mentions evidence-based medicine of course, and I was going to end this article by revealing whether this is a science or a religion. Unfortunately, however, I've run out of space. You'll just have to buy the book – only four volumes and a snip at €1200.

It's all in the timing

Since retiring I've had more time for my hobby, songwriting, and last year my musical friends and I returned to the Edinburgh Fringe with a mixture of humour and history. A sense of timing is essential for both songs and jokes, and ours was, mercifully, still just about intact. Comic timing is age-related: youthful comedians rarely pause for breath because their noisy young audiences have fast reactions – something that my wife and I noticed when we became midweek theatregoers. Busloads of schoolchildren certainly liven up Shakespeare, and as we recently discovered, intense contemporary drama is much more fun when its sex scenes are accompanied by slurping sounds from the stalls.

The skill of slowing down comes with age. Its supreme exponent was a music-hall comedian whom I saw in London in the 1970s after I attended a MRCOG course. His name was Max Wall and he had become, in his late sixties, a darling of the smart set. What I remember most about his very funny one-man show was the long silences. "Not a bad house … for a Tuesday," he remarked, watching us intently, like a matador, ready to skewer us at any moment. In the second half he came on as Professor Wallofski, a grotesque parody of the pianist Franz Liszt. Come to think of it, he may have sowed the seed of our recent Fringe show, which was all about Frederic Chopin.

Ask me later

A sense of timing is also important for doctors, as we ask our intrusive questions and give our unwelcome advice. General practitioners say that a patient often mentions the real problem only when the consultation is nearly over: this requires another, longer, appointment. One of the benefits of private practice, I'm told, is getting to know a patient properly, something which is almost impossible in the NHS. I've been an NHS patient from time to time, very grateful for the efficiency but aware of being on a conveyer belt. Each professional, however courteous and well-trained, has one eye on the clock. We patients sympathise but it's a shame that we need the hide of a rhinoceros to mention a problem that isn't already on the computer.

From my days in practice, one of my most memorable patients was a woman with abdominal pain that had led to some major operations, not all gynaecological. No pathology had been found but for some reason I found it hard to discharge her from the clinic. She answered no to all my questions but eventually phoned to ask for an urgent appointment, at which her history of childhood sexual abuse slowly emerged. An extreme example, yes, but it illustrated that however cordial your handshake, a patient may need a long time to decide if she can trust you.

A long time in politics

Timing is even more important at the medicopolitical level. I can remember when decisions about running a service were taken by consultants (yes, really) but even in those days achieving consensus was no easy matter. I admired my senior colleagues who had mastered the art. During most of the debate they kept quiet, and then they chose exactly the right moment to intervene. Suddenly we found ourselves agreeing, grateful that they had summed up the mood of the meeting and rarely realising that they had got what they wanted.

Today the big decisions are made, not by doctors or managers, but by politicians, whose timing extends only as far as the next election. They know that any worthwhile project to improve the nation's health takes a couple of decades but they need instant results. In the game of political football the teams change ends every five years and key players are substituted more frequently than that: England has had 12 Health Secretaries in the last 23 years. Sadly, their short-term gimmickry makes real change all the slower.

This must be why the introduction of relicensing has taken three times as long as the Second World War. Somewhere in our attic are drafts of the first RCOG working party report on revalidation, which I helped to write in 1999. We proposed a process that was essentially the same as the one now due for completion in 2016. What happened during those 17 years? The websites became slicker, the entrepreneurs moved in and some of us suffered terminal disillusionment. Imagine the uproar if the response times of the doctors soon to undergo revalidation matched that of the people in charge of the process.

Ruby wedding

Our 40th wedding anniversary is only a few weeks away. This is one of life's more obscure milestones. Everyone knows about the big jubilees – the 25th is silver and the 50th is gold – but what about those in between? My wife and I used to get this information from a dishtowel which listed all the anniversary gift suggestions from 1 year (paper) to 10 years (tin) and beyond, but now, of course, we have Google. No need to rummage through the airing cupboard to discover that it takes only 8 years to achieve bronze, 15 for crystal, 30 for pearl, and of course 40 for ruby.

Wikipedia tells you more than you want to know. The flowers for next month's bouquet should be gladioli, though I suspect my wife would not appreciate their whiff of Dame Edna. Apparently most of the anniversary symbols, apart from gold and silver, were dreamed up by the American National Retail Jewellers Association in 1937. They decided that diamonds at 60 years should be followed by blue sapphires at 65 and platinum at 70, presumably in the hope that recklessness increases with age even if spending power doesn't. And they evidently had a graveyard sense of humour with the gift for the 80th anniversary being oak.

Fashions change

I know what you're thinking: how can anyone possibly be old enough to have been married for 40 years? Well, it's a generation thing. Back in the 1960s it was not uncommon for medical students to marry each other – though competition was fierce with only one woman to five men. By waiting until a year or two after graduation, my fiancée and I thought we were showing restraint but we were babes by today's standards, and indeed by those of the 19th century. My yellowing copy of the Drife family tree shows that most of my distant ancestors, all Scottish shepherds, were well into their 30s before tying the knot.

It's disconcerting to realise that your life choices are determined not by the planets but by social trends, documented by the Office of National Statistics (ONS). In 1970 the mean age at first marriage for men was approaching its all-time low of 24.4 years. So much for my self-image of rugged individualism: in 1973 I was only just above the national average.

The figure then climbed to its present level of 32.1 years. The corresponding ages for women were 22.4 in 1970 and 30.0 in 2010. The antenatal clinic has changed a lot since we became clients in 1975, when the BMJ defined a woman over 35 as an 'elderly primigravida'.

Whole-time equivalents

Some of the current figures from the Office for National Statistics (ONS) are depressing: only 66% of marriages reach the crystal anniversary, and 20% of today's divorcees have already been divorced at least once. The ONS does not break down these data by social class, much less by medical specialty, but I have the clinical impression that obstetricians and gynaecologists tend to stay married. The only evidence I've found to back this up is a paper in the *New England Journal of Medicine (NEJM* 1997;336:800–3). Among doctors who graduated from Johns Hopkins University between 1944 and 1960, the incidence of divorce by 30 years of marriage was highest among psychiatrists and lowest among paediatricians and pathologists. I guess OB/GYNs were among the 'others' in the middle. I know this has little relevance to the UK in the present day, but that's the norm for published evidence, isn't it?

"What's it like being married for 40 years?" I hear you ask. I don't feel qualified to answer because, really, we've cheated. At the start, each of us was resident on call for one night in two or three, so on average we slept together once a week – and sleep we did. As an obstetric registrar, I seem to remember living in hospital with the family visiting at weekends. After that, academic life meant going to conferences rather than doing the school run. By my reckoning we've accumulated enough credits for a china anniversary at most. The benefit of this out-dated lifestyle comes when you retire, and discover that you still like each other.

Diary check, dear

We're planning a quiet jubilee. Few restaurants are open on the date itself (a Sunday) or on Mondays, so it will be a Ruby Tuesday – very 1960s. We won't dress up in our kaftans, however, and it will be just the two of us. No flotilla on the river Thames, no firework display and (sorry, jewellers) no rubies. I offered, of course, but she says red isn't her colour. Thanks, love.

Girls, girls, girls

When our first grandchild was born a few months ago we already knew that the baby was a girl. Even before the news was confirmed by the wonders of ultrasound, we had sort of expected it. All the other recent arrivals in our extended family have been girls: a grand-niece for us, a second grand-daughter for my songwriting partner (a collaborator is almost a blood relative), and a daughter for my wife's language tutor (related to us by the future perfect subjunctive, a tie that my wife says is thicker than water).

Advance knowledge of the baby's gender is said to help the bonding process, though I doubt that it can make much difference to such a primordial emotion. What it does do is decide the colour of the babygro. 'Pink for a girl' is a tradition that goes all the way back to the 1940s, but it gives pause to modern grandparents who aspire to gender-blindness. Is it the first step in social imprinting? Should we go instead for black or yellow? But then she might grow up to be a Goth or a Liberal Democrat. Not that there's anything wrong with either, of course. In the end we chose a blue-free pattern.

Take that

Having realised that mine was the first UK generation to be colour-coded after inspection of its genitalia, I began to wonder how the expectations of the 1940s and 1950s have affected me. Our school had two doors with 'GIRLS' or 'BOYS' carved in stone above them. The playground was divided by railings and inside, at least in some classrooms, the girls sat on one side and the boys on the other. This sexual segregation, however, was half-hearted compared to Scotland's religious demarcation. There was a separate school for Roman Catholics even in our small village.

At our primary school the girls tended to be at the top of the class, but not for long. Academic achievement is determined less by brainpower than by parental expectations, and in that mining community girls were not expected to go to university. Nor were boys, come to that, and the frustration felt by the teachers was obvious even to us kids. On leaving for a senior school I won most of the prizes, which prompted a dose of corporal punishment – 'the strap' – from a vengeful lady maths teacher. (On my hands: we weren't barbarians.) She and I both knew that my talent for algebra was vastly inferior to that of her favourite pupil, a quiet girl who started a family shortly afterwards.

Catwalk interns

Things have changed a lot in 50 years. In the mining industry women have yet to break the glass ceiling (if that's the right cliché) but they are well established in the professions. Among medical specialties the pace of feminisation has varied, with sexual and reproductive health in the vanguard and surgery in the rear. General medicine is somewhere in between. When I took ill in The Netherlands a couple of years ago I was admitted to a splendid hospital and was unsurprised to find that the whole team of junior physicians was female. What took me aback was that they all dressed like fashion models. Even with my life in danger I found it hard to take the ward round seriously.

Mr Lazy

Aha, I hear you say, that's irrational masculine prejudice: as a bow tie wearer you're hardly in a position to criticise Jimmy Choo shoes. OK, point taken, but I do think that one of the few biological differences between the male and female brains is an interest in clothes. This was why, no matter how long I hung around the delivery suite as consultant on call, I could never really join in the midwives' conversations. My wife remembers what she was wearing on every significant occasion during our married life. So could I, I suppose, but only because I make each jacket last a decade.

This is not a big deal but there is one male/female difference that worries me. In my youth I always had my nose in a book, but somewhere along the line the habit died. Today the Amazon man calls regularly but his parcels are all for my wife. We're not atypical. Most fiction is bought by women and book groups around the country are predominantly, if not exclusively, female. Being bored by stories seems to be a feature of the ageing male. Perhaps reading the Mr Men to our new grand-daughter will reignite my enthusiasm for literature.

Learning from the Boss

I've always assumed that the typical reader of *And finally…* is a young trainee taking a quick peek before tackling a particularly fiendish CPD question. I sympathise with this person. On my run-up to the MRCOG I had to nerve myself to open a journal – gosh, am I really supposed to know all this stuff? In the 1970s there was no *TOG* but we had *BJOG,* then called the *Journal of Obstetrics and Gynaecology of the British Commonwealth* and filled with papers by great men (mainly) on subjects ranging from William Hunter to electron microscopy.

But time has moved on. Gone are the days when specialists hit peak knowledge level on the day of the exam and went into slow decline for the next three decades. Today continuing medical education is for all ages, and *TOG* is also read by people with bifocals. I feel foolish for failing to understand this until now. It was only after some oblique remarks from my contemporaries that I realised they had been eavesdropping on my attempts to relate to the younger generation. So if my tone is a little strained this time, that's why.

Retired fellows

Sociologists and marketing gurus are keen to pigeonhole birth cohorts, beginning with baby boomers and continuing through generation X to today's generation Z. (After them, what comes next? Perhaps sociologists will give up and get real jobs.) In modern Britain, communication between generations is subtly discouraged. The young are too busy texting and WhatsApp-ing one another to talk to the old and we, the middle-aged, are too self-conscious to say anything. Phrases such as "dance like your Dad" make us fear we'll be laughed at, and despite being interested in what our children do, we wouldn't dream of applying to become their Facebook friends.

Professionally, my happiest memory of good communication was in a hospital canteen where a big table was set aside for us doctors. It was a small hospital and trainees and consultants from all specialties ate and chatted together. I still remember the wit and wisdom of a surgeon who had gained much of his experience in Africa. What a lot we learned. But by the 1980s our special table had gone, a despised symbol of medical elitism.

As a consultant you have a boss/apprentice relationship with your younger colleagues but when you retire, this disappears. We retirees huddle together, sharing our new interests and reading our journal, *The Oldie*. Should there be an edition for doctors, the *Medical Oldie* (or better, *The Moldie)*? I doubt if it would do well. Meetings of the BMA Retired Members' Forum and the RCOG Retired Fellows and Members Society rarely have standing room only. Many retirees want to get away from medicine completely and the rest of us feel uncomfortable at being labelled as retired.

Me and Bruce

Generational stereotyping can be fun (last week I noticed a car sticker: GRUMPY OLD GIT ON BOARD) but it too is changing. Age groups used to be defined by their tastes in music – punk or symphonies – but in 2013 things have become blurred. At the Saturday orchestral concerts in Leeds Town Hall there are a fair number of young people in the audience, and although I don't see myself joining the Justin Bieber fan club just yet, I can reveal that I recently attended a rock concert in the new Leeds Arena.

What a night it was. Bruce Springsteen, who will have turned 64 by the time you read this, electrified 13,500 of us with a three-hour, high-energy performance which included leaping backwards onto the outstretched arms of his adoring fans. Occasionally he stepped away from the microphone and left the singing to the 13,499 people in the room who knew all the words. Not me, sadly, but I was impressed that those who did ranged in age from about 7 to 70. Near the end Bruce pulled a whole family on stage to dance with him.

The seniors' spot

Comparing an RCOG meeting to a concert on the Wrecking Ball Tour may be stretching things slightly, but I think we have something to learn from the Boss. Why not, as well as encouraging trainees to submit 10-minute papers, invite similar contributions from the ranks of the retired? I'm sure we could stick to time if we really had to, and we might surprise everyone (including ourselves) by having something interesting to say. A panel of trainees could decide on the best Senior Paper, and the prize could be a bag of Werther's Originals.

Just a minute

January has had two fixed dates in my diary for a few years now. One is our regional trainees' meeting and the other is Burns Night. As the latter is a mystery to most non-Scottish readers, I'd better explain briefly. Robert Burns, an 18th century Scots songwriter and poet, was the Elvis Presley of his day – a country boy with talent and sex-appeal who became famous, died at 39 (Presley died at 42) and is now an icon. Today Burns Suppers (think Elvis Convention with haggis) are held on or near his birthday on 25th January. Without them, the northern winter would be a miserable prospect.

Which is probably the reason why the Yorkshire trainees also meet in January. To keep their spirits up they have clinical lectures, a pep-talk about the latest national initiatives for enhancing the postgraduate experience, and prizes for the best trainee presentation and poster. In the evening, I believe, the trainees socialise, which counts as peer-group support. Unlike Burns Night there's no haggis or whisky, though I can't help feeling that a glass or two of Glen McCalman would help those national initiatives go down.

A deanery is born

The Yorkshire Region has a population almost as big as Denmark's and a single postgraduate deanery, which didn't exist when I arrived in Leeds in 1990. Indeed the word 'deanery' first appeared in the *BMJ* as late as 1998. (*The Lancet* had it a century earlier, but only in relation to the Church of England.) Although postgraduate deans had come earlier they hadn't been invented when I qualified in 1971. When the posts appeared in the mid-1970s they were seen as a relaxing way for consultants to spend a few years before retirement. All that changed in the 1990s. I remember how shocked we were on an interview panel for a new dean when one candidate told us she wanted to shake things up. To our credit (and hers) she got the job.

Until then, training had relied on the apprentice system, which we retirees now look back on fondly. We're kidding ourselves, I'm afraid. I also remember being an interview candidate myself in the 1980s and, when asked for my views on postgraduate education, using the word 'shambles'. Some panel members woke up and glared at me and things quickly went downhill, which is why the moment is fixed in my memory. I was right, though. At that time, the Royal Colleges limited themselves to running their membership examinations, university departments organised a few courses, and drug companies did the rest. Yes, today's trainees do far too much box-ticking but believe me, self-directed learning palls after the first decade.

Here comes the judge

The disadvantage of having prizes at the regional meeting is that the organisers need judges. I try to avoid this responsibility because I have the wrong personality for the role. I like to see some good in everyone and I hate to see anyone being disappointed. But I realise I'm in the minority. Today on television nobody can sing, dance, bake a cake or visit the Australian jungle unless they are part of an agonising contest which will leave them in tears. How can viewers bear to watch?

When judging, I become too introspective. What makes a good poster? How do you balance design, science and clinical relevance? Do you deduct marks when the Blu-Tack fails? Published guidance is scanty and can best be summarised as, 'Keep it simple, stupid'. This is easier said than done, and it used to need years of experience, though these days most trainees seem to have got the knack. Perhaps the College now has a KISS module.

Guest chairman

So, Prof, I hear you ask: if you don't like judging and are too old to give a clinical lecture, why is this date still in your diary? Well, I really enjoy meeting the rising generation, but the actual reason is that the organisers need someone to impersonate Nicholas Parsons. One of the sessions is based on 'Just a Minute', the radio show in which panellists have to talk for 60 seconds without hesitation … etc., etc. At the meeting the subjects are non-medical and it's great fun. The competitors (trainees versus consultants) require wit and skill and take it very seriously. For a chairman they need someone who has been listening to Mr Parsons since his show began in 1967, and who has absorbed something of his personality. I'm happy to oblige, and if it means skipping a Burns Supper, so much the better.

The third edition

I've just finished rewriting my two chapters for a well-known postgraduate textbook. The first edition was published in 2004 and the second in 2010, and now, apparently, it's time for a third. I thought that after only 4 years I might get away with a little tweaking here and there, but how wrong I was. My chapters are on maternal and perinatal mortality, and both subjects have changed, if not beyond recognition, then certainly enough to need radical revision and a new cartridge for my printer. (Why do typing errors show up only on paper and never on the screen?)

The changes are all for the better. Global maternal mortality is falling, although I can't help wondering how reliable those improved estimates are. Still, it felt good to be able to revise the numbers downwards. Here in Britain the sudden death of our Confidential Enquiries in 2011 has been followed by the birth of MBRRACE-UK, which is easy to find on Google once you realise that it doesn't begin with an 'E'. It has reinstated the maternal death enquiry and – even better for us textbook-writers – introduced a new way of classifying perinatal deaths. Out go the old systems that took up a whole column in my chapter and unhelpfully categorised most stillbirths as 'unexplained'.

Heroes of the past

The modern textbook is a team effort and I'm just one of the 66 foot-soldiers in this literary task force. How different it seems from the days when I was an MRCOG candidate and our books were written by omniscient single authors. But yet again my memory is playing me false. At the back of high shelves in my study are my old textbooks, and a quick check (standing on a swivel chair – always a challenge) shows that even those god-like authorities had a little help from their friends. I see that in Edinburgh's professorial textbook of the 1960s the chapter on X-rays in pregnancy was written by a radiologist, and going even further back, the legendary Victor Bonney had a co-author for his ground-breaking textbook on gynaecological surgery, first published in 1911.

I'm glad I kept those old books, if only for their prefaces. A favourite with us trainees was *Practical Obstetric Problems*, written by Ian Donald, the pioneer of ultrasound. It was full of his entertaining opinions but he too needed support from co-authors, as he acknowledged in the first edition in 1954: "My views upon the misuse of antibiotics are so strong that I thought it a good plan to seek the help of one whose views are even stronger...". That first preface began: "The art of teaching is the art of sharing enthusiasm" (a motto that should be on every professor's desk) but as edition followed edition the strain began to tell. In 1969 the opening line of his fourth preface was, "A millstone round the neck can carry its wearer into deep waters". Then as now, a new edition was needed every 4–5 years, though I suspect that real medical progress was faster in those days.

The future is paper

A few years ago we were all wondering if books could survive the on-line revolution, but they seem to be doing OK. The journal that I edit receives papers from many countries, and their lists of references often feature the standard American textbook *Williams Obstetrics*, now in its 24th edition. When the book first appeared in 1903, its author, the impressively moustachioed John Whitridge Williams, was chief of obstetrics at the Johns Hopkins Hospital in Baltimore, Maryland. Today the entire 23rd edition can be downloaded for free (or so they say) from various pirate websites. That's immortality for you, Dr Williams.

So what's the attraction? Well, we all need something solid to hang on to, and a heavy book has an air of authority that a smartphone lacks. What's more, a book is finite, with a beginning and an end. It makes MRCOG candidates feel that all they need to do is read it and everything will be fine. The problem, I seem to remember, is staying awake.

That was the deadline that was

Now that my chapters are in, I'm anxiously awaiting the editors' verdict. Theirs will be the only feedback I get. None of the 66 authors will hear from the people who actually read the book. It's our own fault, as we strive for faceless uniformity. If there's a fourth edition, maybe I should follow Donald's example and leaven my death-filled chapters with a few jokes.

On your bike

Excitement is mounting in Yorkshire. Roads have been resurfaced, an official song has been recorded and the T-shirts are on sale. On 5th July the streamlined peloton of the Tour de France will race from Leeds to Harrogate, going the long way round – 190km via Buttertubs Pass, 1725 feet above sea level (much more impressive-sounding than 526 metres). But of course you know all that already. By the time you read this, the event will be history and you may even have seen the highlights on television.

Close up, it seems superhuman. Even with Buttertubs the first stage is classified as 'flat', and stage 2, which passes Holme Moss (the highest radio transmitter in the UK) is officially a 'hill'. Not until they reach the Vosges in eastern France will the competitors face mountains. My two-wheeled excursions to the Co-op seem puny by comparison, but nonetheless they give me a glow of satisfaction. I'm part of the global cycling fraternity. Admittedly I feel closer kinship with the patient pedallers of the Low Countries than with our local macho men, who are tweeting that Le Tour de Yorkshire has chosen a route for cissies.

Call the midwife

The bicycle was once an essential part of maternity equipment, particularly in the East End of London. In the classic 1950's film, *Doctor in the House*, medical student Simon Sparrow is sent off with a temperamental bike on Christmas Eve to attend a para 6 delivering at home in the ironically-named Paradise Buildings. With the midwife snowbound, he delivers the baby himself, while granny provides the endless hot water which was essential to movie childbirth in those days. Giving up on the bike, our hero walks home, after a tear-jerking farewell to the baby, named Simon by his grateful mum.

The same ground was covered more recently by BBC's *Call the Midwife*, and again the bicycle played a starring role. According to Halfords, the series sparked a sales rush for retro-style ladies' bikes, now trendily named the Pendleton range. Taking a retrospective look at my own schooldays I can't recall actually seeing our village midwife on a bicycle but I do remember the moment when she drove past in a car for the first time. It was, I think, a Morris Minor and at a stroke it catapulted her into the upper echelons of society. Cycling keeps you in touch with the people, but driving makes you remote. This must be why the bike is so popular with northern European royal families.

The rise of the eco-warrior

Obstetricians are not traditionally associated with pedal power. Pity. What fun it would have been to dash to a delivery with a front basket full of forceps (or better still, vacuum extractors – the pump being already fixed to the frame). But consultants of my generation felt duty-bound to buy expensive-looking cars, if only for the quiet pleasure of irritating our colleagues in Social Medicine. Shortly before I retired I was surprised by a tap on my window as I sat at the traffic lights. A colleague on a bike was haranguing me about my effect on the planet. We were both facing uphill so the conversation didn't last long, but he followed it with an e-mail. I didn't get rid of my car, but I began to feel guilty about it.

I felt I had no alternative to driving. I lacked the self-confidence (and fitness) of the few doctors who arrived at the hospital in Lycra and took their non-folding bikes into the lift. In retirement I've at last pedalled onto the moral high ground but I still haven't mastered the finer points of urban cycling – ignoring traffic lights, yelling at pedestrians and dicing with death in the rush hour. Does the NHS now have bike sheds? Will Britain ever provide proper cycle lanes? Too late for me.

Beating the boys

I'm looking forward to Le Tour but I regret that it's so male-dominated. Social bicycling is bisexual. My daughter and her husband cycle around London (very flat, London) with our little grand-daughter on one or other pillion. I've heard that Vivienne Westwood, aged 73, also prefers the bike in the capital: after dismounting she changes her shoes. But competitive cycling has its heroines, and the greatest was a girl from Leeds. Beryl Burton (1937–1996) won international titles and in 1967 broke the men's 12-hour time trial record: it would be two years before a man surpassed this. She and her daughter later set a record for the women's tandem. *C'est magnifique*, as we now say in Yorkshire.

179

Talking to the midwives

Next week I shall be giving a lecture to student midwives. A trip to the University of Salford has been an annual fixture in my diary for quite a while, but this could be my last one. A curriculum review is pending. My talk is about maternal mortality, so it's high time I was replaced by someone from MBRRACE-UK, which is about to publish its first report. I'll be sad to stop, though. I've enjoyed my visits. The midwifery students are highly selected and very motivated. They can stand an afternoon of professorial PowerPoint without falling asleep, and there are always some penetrating questions.

Perhaps the curriculum reviewers will do away with lectures altogether. Lecturers have been out of favour with educationalists for as long as I can remember – in fact, longer. On clearing my old office I found a booklet, *The Training of a Doctor,* dated 1948. It was produced by the BMA (not the GMC, interestingly) and it noted that 'several clinical teachers [expressed] doubt of the value of systematic lectures'. Nevertheless it concluded that lectures still had a place, but 'need more forethought and preparation than they are often given at present'. It also suggested that the lecturer should aim at 'relaxing the student's attentive face in an occasional smile'.

The great divide

The most treacherous lecture is the one you've given before, so the BMA's point about forethought and preparation is well taken. Attentive faces are the norm among the student midwives but raising an occasional smile may not be easy. Maternal mortality is never a bundle of laughs, and there's also the problem of the generation gap. Jokey asides require some common ground shared by speaker and audience, but I'm from the last century and some of these women will be young enough to be my grand-daughters. I've found that the only thing that really connects across the generations is sincerity, and this becomes easier as you get older.

Age isn't the only barrier, though. There's also a culture gap. Midwives and doctors see things differently. If you Google the title at the top of this page, almost the first words you see are "empowerment" and "alliances between midwives and women". These days, empowerment is basic to midwives' thinking but it's a dirty word in medicine. Doctors, sick and tired of clichéd accusations about playing God, are trying, with little success, to disempower themselves. And alliances? Surely we obstetricians are on women's side too – and we've always been allied with the midwives, haven't we?

The oldest profession

Well, that depends on how far back you go. Obstetrics is younger than midwifery by several millennia. In Genesis chapter 35, a midwife reassures Jacob's second wife that she will have a son. In chapter 38 a midwife successfully conducts a complicated twin delivery without medical assistance. Physicians don't appear until chapter 50, where their duties are limited to embalming Jacob's dead body, and neither surgeons nor obstetricians are mentioned at all in the Bible. Impressed by my scholarship? Don't be: my grandfather was a clergyman and among the books I inherited was a biblical index.

Fast forward to the 18th century and William Smellie (whose Wikipedia entry, incidentally, does him scant justice). Smellie gave lectures to midwives but also famously endured picturesque insults from some of their number. Fast forward again to 1948, the year of that BMA booklet, and we find tension between midwives and GP obstetricians, who greatly outnumbered consultants. In 1949 a BMJ editorial commented on lack of integration among obstetricians, GPs and midwives and laid some of the blame on the newly-established NHS, for dividing services up. The editorial prophesied: 'We seem indeed to be drifting into the absurd position in which the midwife is looked upon as the specialist in normal and the obstetrician as the specialist in abnormal midwifery'.

What do you mean, 'absurd'?

The drift has been slow but the prophecy has of course come true. Royalty and oligarchs apart, normal deliveries in the UK rarely involve obstetricians. GPs used to say that maternity was the bedrock of their practice and obstetricians once believed you must fully understand the normal before treating the abnormal, but all that has gone. Is the NHS to blame? Maybe, maybe not. In Dublin, where public care is free, 25–30% of women still opt for private obstetricians, but even there the figure is now falling. None of which is directly relevant to next week's lecture. I shall stick to maternal mortality, but perhaps allow myself a little wallow in nostalgia, remembering the days when lecturing to the midwives was part of every registrar's routine.

Forthcoming festivals

I've just downloaded my Leeds University year planner for 2015. (Old habits die hard, even in retirement.) Many of its dates have asterisks indicating religious festivals, almost all of them anonymous. Christmas is named (presumably in case any professors are baffled by the sudden appearance of snowmen on the city's lamp posts) but the others remain mysterious. This worries me. Which of my friends am I going to upset by ignoring their holy days? It doesn't help that the dates change every year and some aren't fixed until the last minute. "For more info", says the year planner. "See the BBC Religion website". Sadly, the BBC Interfaith Calendar has given up the struggle and is having a makeover.

Ancient and modern

We're on more solid ground with secular festivals. Some go back a long way. Guy Fawkes Night was established in 1606 by Act of Parliament after the Gunpowder Plot failed. The Act was repealed in 1859 but fortunately for firework manufacturers the public took no notice. Other national days are more recent. Independence Day in the USA and Bastille Day in France only became official in 1870 and 1880 respectively. Yorkshire Day is even younger, dating from 1975. It falls on 1st August, when the nights are short and canny Tykes can celebrate without having to light expensive rockets.

Many of these special days are very new indeed. Mothering Sunday has been around for ages but now in addition we have Mother's Day, Fathers' Day, Grandparents' Day, Siblings' Day and – most recently – Cousins' Day. How much emotional blackmail can one family stand? Are we all expected to buy one another presents? I'm a father, granddad and brother with several cousins, but I can only wear one pair of socks at a time.

Global awareness

Calm down, I hear you say, it's just American commercialism and we can ignore it. Perhaps so, but there's a serious side to all this celebration. The United Nations, no less, has decided that "awareness days" are a way to highlight important issues, and it has produced a list of dates with good causes attached. There are days dedicated to everything from social justice, widows and refugees to wildlife, migratory birds and toilets. Occasionally the mood lightens: 20th March is the International Day of

Happiness and 30th April is Jazz Day. I'm pleased to see that English Language Day is on Shakespeare's birthday and International Literacy Day is on mine. Coincidence or what?

There is of course a World Health Day and there are several disease days to raise the world's awareness of cancer, tuberculosis, malaria, hepatitis, diabetes and, less predictably, autism and Down syndrome. Our specialty is also represented. May 23rd is Obstetric Fistula Day and 11th October is the International Day of the Girl Child. That last one has wiped the patronising smile off my face. Maybe there is some point to all this global awareness-raising, even if it won't produce results overnight.

Specialty days

When it comes to the nitty-gritty of women's health, the specialist societies take the lead. Endometriosis Awareness Week is in March, Infertility Awareness Week in April and World Ovarian Cancer Day in May. At the end of June the International Continence Society organises World Continence Week, which last year included Bladder Diary Day. They all deserve our support, of course, and we non-subspecialists don't want to be accused of favouritism. We shall have to spend the whole of next spring wearing an expression of deep concern.

With only 365 days in the year there are bound to be clashes and, to be honest, some organisations are a bit greedy. The International Menopause Society has designated the whole of October as World Menopause Month, with 18th October as World Menopause Day. But hold on – the National Cancer Institute has October down as National Breast Cancer Awareness Month, with October 17th as National Mammography Day. Will there be lawsuits? I hope not. Perhaps they can share a multi-coloured ribbon.

If you can't beat 'em ...

Dare I ask, what about us? Nurses have an International Day and so do midwives, but few countries recognise Doctors Day. The RCOG should take the initiative. We could have an International Day of the Trainee, when your Educational Supervisor has to bring you a present or, if they forget, sign you up as competent in a module of your choice. And for me and my contemporaries, a Retired Consultants Day, when young colleagues have to ask for our opinion about something and continue to look interested while we give it. Well, a man can dream.

Learning the lingo

My wife has just started Spanish classes. It's years since we visited Iberia or South America but she enjoys learning languages, and the Instituto Cervantes makes part-time learners feel welcome. The Institute, run by the Spanish government and with branches in over 20 countries, is named after Miguel de Cervantes, a Spanish surgeon's son who wrote the first modern European novel. Volume 2 of *Don Quixote* appeared in 1615. Now, four centuries later, there are said to be about 100,000 new novels published each year in English alone. Crikey. Miguel has a lot of answer for.

The Spanish word for language is "lengua". The French is "langue", the Italian "lingua" and the Romanian "limba" – all derived, of course, from the Latin word for tongue. With their shared Roman roots, southern European languages seem deceptively simple to us Brits. The slang word "lingo" in my title sums up our lack of respect for them, and indeed our laziness about learning any foreign language. Why bother, we say, when cities all over the world, including Oxford and Cambridge, are full of English language schools catering for eager students.

Doktoro Esperanto

Back in the 1960s at Edinburgh Medical School there was an attempt to promote an alternative to English as the universal language. The graffiti in one of the toilets included a small poster saying, "Lerni la lingvon Esperanto". A wit had written underneath, "Gette stuffato", and that seemed to be the end of that intellectual debate. Pity. I've always felt that a neutral lingua franca is a great idea. I even bought "Teach Yourself Esperanto" but sadly never got round to reading it.

I now know that "Doktoro Esperanto" was the pen-name of Dr Zamenhof, a Jewish ophthalmologist who wanted to ease tensions among the Poles, Russians, Germans, Jews and others in his native city of Bialystock. Part of the problem was that each community had its own language, and in 1887 he published a completely new one. "Esperanto" means "hoping" (oh dear, another Latin-based vocabulary) but as it turned out, hope was short-lived. In the 1930s various nationalists denounced the language and both Hitler and Stalin executed its users. Then as now, winning hearts and minds to internationalism was an uphill struggle.

Good moaning!

At school I learned French, like everyone who wanted to enter university, but really it has been of limited help to me. I soon found, faced with a French visitor in the outpatient clinic, that I was ill-prepared to take a gynaecological history. (The word for "period", I discovered, is "regle": why hadn't I been told?) Today schoolboy French is no longer universal – in 2011 only 40% of pupils in England took a GCSE in any foreign language. Realising this, I've had to mothball one of my comedy standbys, a joke in Franglais that once had them rolling in the aisles. I wouldn't dare use it in an after-dinner speech now, except for an audience of senior citizens.

But even for my generation a schoolboy standard was all we wanted to achieve. We knew that if you speak with a heavy foreign accent people will smile at your mistakes and won't take offence. The same principle applies when foreigners speak our language. Visiting France recently, my wife and I found that one of the staff in a local tourist office spoke as if she had come straight from Buckingham Palace. One slip would have been a disaster but fortunately her English was perfect. She must have wondered, though, why we exited backwards, bowing.

Accents send messages of which the speaker may not be aware. The English now being taught around the globe tends to have an American inflection. Here in Britain immigration has broadened the range of accents while some impenetrable rural dialects have disappeared. In the past ambitious people (with exceptions, like Alan Bennett) worked hard to lose their regional accents but I don't hear much about elocution teachers these days. And we Scots are lucky because our brogue is widely perceived as reassuring for a doctor, or indeed any professional. Perhaps those language academies should move from Oxford and Cambridge to Inverness.

An ongoing stakeholder?

I'm tempted to join my wife at her classes. Why don't I, then? To be honest, I'm still trying to master English. During my forty years in academic medicine I've had to get to grips with bureaucratic jargon, political doublespeak, sociological mumbo-jumbo, a mind-numbing succession of acronyms and the ebb and flow of politically correct terminology. After all that, Spanish should be easy, but I need a break.

Offline education

Today I'm off to a lunchtime lecture. It will be a leisurely affair involving a three-course meal and, I hope, a pleasant chat with fellow retirees afterwards. I feel a bit mean telling you this, because I know how much it contrasts with lunchtime talks for working doctors. I remember how I always used to arrive late, clutching a polystyrene cup and hoping to get halfway through a sandwich before my bleep – or mobile – forced me to make that crouching run for the door. More often than not I wasn't there at all, delayed by the clinic or the silly idea that lunch is for wimps, even when it includes the Grand Round.

The biggest difference now, though, is that the talks I attend would carry no Brownie points towards revalidation. Today's subject is the history of Damascus, "the oldest continuously inhabited city on the planet". Last month I heard our local bishop discussing the reorganisation of the Diocese of Leeds, and next week I'll be listening to Tariq Ali (a revolutionary firebrand in the 1960s) reflecting on the Arab Spring. Imagine putting that lot in your personal development file and trying to justify it at your annual appraisal.

Primitive urges

Does this seem a strange way of spending my leisure time? You may be surprised to hear that these lectures are popular. There's a waiting list for the Damascus talk, even though we've been warned that the speaker will have more slides than usual. Sometimes my wife and I travel a long distance to attend an afternoon of varied lectures, and the hall is always packed, mainly by senior citizens like ourselves. Why do we do it? Part of the reason, I think, is that after a lifetime of specialisation you wake up to the fact that there's a great big world out there, full of interesting things, and you want to catch up.

But there's also a more primordial motivation. Human beings are herd animals, hardwired to behave in certain ways. One of these is to be part of a crowd of like-minded people who are being talked at. In the past this urge was satisfied by going to church and sitting through long sermons. And we've all seen old photos of large open-air audiences listening to a politician addressing them without the aid of a microphone. Those days may be gone but our instincts remain. Today people pay eye-watering ticket prices for stand-up comedians who serve up wit, wisdom and political insight to their devoted fans – most of them young. After a certain age, though, you lose your taste for smart-alecs and four-letter words, and return to your roots in the lecture hall.

The generation thing

We could get our new knowledge from the web, of course. On-line learning is popular with medical royal colleges, particularly those with far-flung members in developing countries. It's popular too with us sofa-based oldies in British cities, especially when the alternative is Downton Abbey. But an iPad, despite its stunning technology, is not very different from a book. It's a solitary pleasure. Even if it enables distant interaction, that's not the same as being face-to-face. Mind you, I worry that the next generation can't tell the difference. I first noticed this some years ago at a pub lunch with my daughter's friends: at one point everyone around the table (except me) was gazing at their mobile phone and smiling. What's the matter, Dad? No friends or flat battery?

The thing about a lecture is that it's a live performance, requiring adrenaline from the speaker and – ideally – producing some in the listener to make it memorable. But just like that pub, audience members today quietly check for messages or even log on to their social network. It's the height of rudeness. Lecturers notice but are too polite to comment. Time to roll back the clock and give teachers bits of chalk to throw at persistent offenders.

Living in a silo

Our local medical society organises monthly lectures and I'm trying to bridge the generation gap by encouraging students and trainees to join. Everyone says this is a good idea but it's hard to convince young doctors that it's worthwhile turning up. Do aspiring obstetricians really want to hear about advances in, say, cardiology or orthopaedic surgery? Depressingly, the answer's no but I'll keep trying. These lectures don't tick official boxes but my word, they're interesting. Yes, we're all working in specialty silos but it's good to get some exercise occasionally by climbing up and peeping over the edge.

Pioneers versus mockers

Some buses in Edinburgh are now enlivened by huge pictures of James Young Simpson on their sides. Almost 168 years after he pioneered chloroform anaesthesia he's still a hero in his home town. Inspired by my bus-spotting, I went on-line to browse *The Lancet* of 1847 and was amazed at how quickly the news of his discovery had spread. His enthusiasm for painless childbirth was criticised on various grounds, some of them religious, but nobody mocked it. His other ideas, however, including an obstetric vacuum extractor (which didn't work) and an "orthomatron" to cure uterine retroversion, were quickly scorned as quackery.

Mockers of pioneers don't always get it right. As Simpson was sliding under the table after his first sniffs of chloroform, Elizabeth Blackwell was beginning her medical studies in America. When she became the first woman to receive a medical degree in the USA this news, too, travelled fast but it caused amusement, not outrage. In Britain *Punch* published an admiring poem which suggested giving her a gold-handled parasol. This patronising joke was recycled by *The Lancet* when Blackwell planned her own medical college. It commented that the insignia should be "a pair of bracelets twined round the handle of a parasol". No sillier, I suppose, than a serpent on a stick, still the emblem of the BMA.

Words and pictures

Some mockery can endure. William Smellie, the 18th century obstetrician, is commemorated in our College as the "master of midwifery" but few of us can remember any specific words he said or wrote. The quotation attached to him (and hinted at in this column recently) came from his rival, Mrs Nihel, who also wrote a treatise on midwifery. She called him "a great horse-godmother of a he-midwife". Her invective was not original (the Oxford English Dictionary dates "horse-godmother" back to 1569) but her words have been preserved over the years by those who believe, like her, that men should leave midwifery to women.

Insults added colour to old journals but they've now been replaced, at least in the lay press, by pictures. Photos of duck houses and bacon sandwiches aren't grounds for libel but they can help destroy political careers. Even medical pioneers need to be careful. After the first UK heart transplant in 1968 (the year of the "I'm backing Britain" campaign) the surgeons appeared at a press conference laughing and holding little Union Jacks. *Private Eye* added witty speech balloons and bang went their credibility. Too late, they took advice from a public relations man but the damage was done. Years later they were still upset about it.

The pioneering psyche

The first surgeon to transplant a human heart, in 1967, was Christian Barnaard. He was one of several doctors working in the field, but it was he who dared to do the operation. What drives such pioneers, I wonder? In his case, fame seems to have been the spur. He loved the post-operative media attention and when his travels brought him to Edinburgh the lecture hall was packed. Some questions from us students were hostile and we were surprised that he struggled to answer them. He must have been so focussed that he lost sight of the bigger picture.

Not so pioneers in our own specialty. Patrick Steptoe and Robert Edwards managed to combine single-mindedness with worldly wisdom, which is a difficult trick. Wisdom says, "If you haven't succeeded after nine years, forget it". The pair ploughed on regardless but were worldly enough to meet their critics head-on when the breakthrough came.

Both sides now

As a young researcher I fancied myself as a pioneer. I remember my MD supervisor telling about a new idea: "Everyone says it's crazy, so I think I'm onto something". It didn't change the world but it led to a BMJ paper on measurement of breast volume – and a tsunami of mockery. Later, when I wrote about prophylactic mastectomy, one British tabloid made me its "wally of the week". I still kid myself that I helped pave the way for Angelina Jolie, 20 years later.

Mostly, though, I've been one of the mockers. Underwater birth, minimal access surgery and evidence based medicine (EBM) all inspired me to satire, now lost in various electronic archives. Some mockees didn't notice (my article on underwater caesarean section provoked a request for further details) but the fathers of EBM turned out to have a sense of humour. Writing in Christmas issues of the BMJ they hilariously sent up their foes and, delightfully, themselves. Pioneers *and* mockers. Now that really is impressive.

My latest book

Regular readers will know that I have a book coming out. I hope the phrase "regular readers" doesn't sound presumptuous but some people have told me that they read *And finally* quite frequently, or at least occasionally. I've noticed that they always say this with a guilty air. I wonder why? Perhaps they feel that when you're reading something it's bad form to sneak a look at the last page to see how it all turns out. But *TOG* isn't a mystery magazine – indeed, transparency is its watchword – so there must be another reason.

It can't be that this column has no educational value: I learn a lot from writing it. It must be because it has no accompanying CPD questions. I hesitate to mention this in case I'm asked to provide some, which is a scary thought. The worst thing about being a medical author is being asked, after you've written your exquisitely nuanced article, for a list of "true or false" statements based on it. Few things are completely true or completely false, and as a teacher I detested this method of examining students. What our profession needs, I would thunder, is wise doctors who understand shades of grey, not geeks who think in black and white.

Multiple choice questions are almost as bad but I've drafted a few, just as an experiment. They're based on the last five years of *And finally*. Ready?

Q1. Professor Drife's mother's maiden name is: (a) Smith, (b) Jones, (c) Mitford (d) Middleton (e) Cholmondley-Farquharson

Q2. The River Dryfe is situated in: (a) Cumbria (b) Scotland (c) Northumberland (d) Yorkshire (e) all of the above.

Q3. A 40th wedding anniversary bouquet should contain: (a) frangipani (b) gladioli (c) begonias (d) organic daisies (e) bleeding heartwines.

Gosh, this is fun. At last I've discovered the joys of question-setting. (The answers, by the way, are all "b"s. Just like the questions, I hear you say.)

The promotional tour

But I see that this format is already out of date, as *TOG* is introducing Single Best Answer (SBA) questions even as I write. It's tough, keeping this column at the cutting edge. Before I re-draft my CPD section, let me return to my new book. Regular readers will also know that it's the third edition of a textbook, that I'm one of the 66 authors and that my chapters were submitted in January 2014. Such is the breakneck pace of academic publishing that they'll be only two years out of date when you read them. In the interim I've been looking at modern methods of book promotion. Medical publishers are way behind the times with these, probably because their authors can't get study leave to do promotional tours. As a retiree, however, I'm more than willing to step in.

Leeds is quite near Manchester, so I can easily pop over to Media City in Salford and plug the book on *BBC Breakfast*. I have several black-and-white photos of myself as a cute toddler and a gawky medical student and, like all my contemporaries, a supply of hilarious anecdotes about the old days. The interviewers won't have to read the book unless they want to: I can supply a tweetable synopsis in layperson's language.

As for book signings, the fact that I'm left-handed needn't be a problem. I'm willing to try forging the signatures of my 65 co-authors but the queue might get a bit restive and I'd prefer just to sign my own chapters – there's room for a dedication and some kisses, and I'm working on a doodle.

The book launch itself must be really special. I suggest having a London bookshop open its doors on the stroke of midnight, and organising a queue of excited buyers dressed as obstetricians and gynaecologists – scrub suits for some, bow ties for others and everyone bare below the elbows.

The medical book festival

When the initial media frenzy dies down it will be time for me to tour the book festivals. These are currently popular across the UK but I doubt if the fashion will last. Writing, not speaking, is what authors are good at and even their most adoring fans will eventually tire of asking them where they get their ideas or whether they do their best work before breakfast.

The literary circuit is increasingly turning to people who aren't full-time writers but have interesting jobs, and what job could be more interesting than ours? I confidently predict that a gynaecologist in the main marquee will swiftly empty the tea tent, and that at question time there will be standing room only. This will be when I announce that the film rights are still available and that we're already working on turning it into a musical.

Do it yourself

Do consultants still have secretaries? I suspect the answer is: "Some do, some don't, and most share". At least that's the impression I got recently after trying to phone colleagues who were no longer responding to emails. To be honest, I was surprised to find that secretaries still exist in the NHS. Several years ago, just before I retired, our hospital was proposing to replace them with a trust-wide electronic dictation system. This met united resistance from consultants and secretaries, who pointed out that theirs was the core relationship that kept the service going. I'm told the plan was eventually shelved because of problems with the voice recognition system. Pity. Judging by the subtitles on television news programmes, the resulting letters would have been hilarious.

But of course secretaries do much more than type. Mine taught me a lot, including the system I still use for organising appointments. An experienced secretary has a network of contacts who know how the hospital really works. She (in my day it was always "she", never "he") would protect you from time-wasters – and from yourself. Irate letters dictated in the heat of the moment went to the bottom of the pile until you cooled down. Indeed, she could sometimes stop you in mid-paragraph by just raising an eyebrow. I hope this skill is still classed as "essential" in a shared secretary's job specification.

Just shred it, professor

In retirement I have to do it all myself. Electronic gadgetry is no help. Even with a spam filter there's a load of incoming messages to delete. Billets-doux from every hotel and theatre I've ever booked on-line. Ungrammatical invitations from open-access journals with unlikely American addresses. Circulars from the university and the hospital, telling me that the sandwich found in the photocopier has been now claimed and that the issues with the web-based outpatient booking system are being urgently addressed. And all those pharmacy updates – reading them would be a full-time job. No wonder the juniors are exhausted.

What I can't do alone, though, is chuck things out. The boxes of papers I brought home when I cleared my office are still in a bulging cupboard, waiting for some ruthless secretary to dispose of them. How can I decide what to recycle and what to preserve? Opening those files is like looking into a lost world – page after page of perfectly punctuated correspondence written by people who could spell. An agenda without bullet points – gosh, how long ago was that? This is history, but not quite old enough to be digitised.

Personal organiser

Never mind. I've discovered a task I can manage unaided – conference organising. Normally this is a secretary's big chance to shine and be appreciated. At the end of a conference dinner the official host will stand up, thank the person who has done all the hard work and present her with a bouquet. The delegates' applause will be heartfelt and prolonged. They know that without her input the speakers would have ended up on the wrong campus, the buses would have been late and the meals would have had no vegetarian option.

My introduction to this stressful world came early in my career. At medical school I was part of a small committee which inherited the task of running a summer school in medical research techniques for overseas students. Shepherding our visitors to the electron microscopes was the easy part. Organising their late-night parties was more challenging, and counselling them about personal problems was, frankly, a nightmare. In those days, when someone asked you how to apply for political asylum, you couldn't simply google the answer.

Never say never again. A mere thirty years later I was stepping up to the plate once more with the Leeds bid to host the RCOG British Congress. My wife and I scouted locations for the Accompanying Persons Programme and selected photos for the submission document (a wow factor is essential for impressing the judges). At the meeting itself the professional organiser took charge. My job was to walk around looking calm and wearing a large rosette.

Rediscovering Leeds

So when our travelling club visited Leeds last year, I felt I already had all the basic skills. I just needed a crash course on the city's one-way system, an update on sports bars and some expert advice about beauty spas. I even walked into a shopping mall unaccompanied. Had I still had a secretary these exhilarating learning experiences would have passed me by. Doing it myself was fun. It gave my emails that all-important personal touch, and of course we saved money on the bouquet.

The non-flying Scotsman

If everything goes according to plan, this article should appear in July, at the start of the holiday season. Years ago, while our children were at school, July was the month in which we joined the queue for the cross-channel ferry, clutching instructions in French about how to find our gite. After the kids left home, our routine changed and my summers were spent covering colleagues' leave and admiring patients' suntans. As we chatted about their distant holiday destinations I felt the odd twinge of envy, always outweighed by relief at avoiding the airport experience.

Does anyone really like airports? I mean, in the way that many of us relish seaports or railway stations even if we're not going anywhere. Airports filled me with anxiety long before their police forces began displaying automatic weapons. The rest of the staff, though unarmed, seemed generally uncaring – except in Manchester, the last bastion of friendliness. I don't know which I disliked more: the faraway airports with their endless bureaucracy or the heart-sinking return to the UK, queuing for ages to be allowed back into my own country.

The class struggle

Worse, though, were the planes. I did most of my flying while Britain's obesity epidemic was gathering pace. My fellow passengers began to encroach from all sides, particularly from the seat in front, which would be tilted back as far as possible soon after take off. As a consultant to the World Health Organisation (WHO) I gained extensive experience of the back rows of economy class. Doctors who work for WHO seem to believe that flying business class to a poor country is morally indefensible, and WHO indulges their masochism by finding really cramped seats. After five years of claustrophobia and two hospital admissions for thromboembolism, I was ready to jack it in. No more moral high ground for me.

194

I finally gave up flying 3 years ago in Copenhagen at a global congress on contraception. Several jet-loads of family planners had touched down simultaneously and the arrivals staff were overwhelmed. After we extricated ourselves from the melee, my wife and I agreed that our return trip would be by boat. This turned out to involve a train ride all the way across Denmark (which looked delightful in the sunshine) and some useful life lessons: (1) don't try to walk from Esbjerg station to the harbour with your suitcases – it's further than it looks on the map; (2) overnight ferries have a wide range of sleeping accommodation, most of it designed to appeal to the cost-conscious; (3) an obliging steward can produce an instant upgrade to first class. That's something you can't get at 30 000 feet.

See Europe by rail

Sadly, those lessons are already out of date. In 2014, the Esbjerg–Harwich route ceased to exist after 160 years, and today there's no direct sea link between the UK and Scandinavia. So much for our Viking heritage. On the other hand, the Channel Tunnel makes the rest of Europe more accessible by train. My last WHO assignment was in 2013 – just before my Copenhagen conversion – and I was already researching no-fly options for my destination, Moldova. London–Zurich by rail (8 hours) and then a bus to Chisinau (38 hours)? Trains all the way (49 hours)? Perhaps not. In the end, I took an Intercity-Express train to Munich and flew from there. I came home by air, but regretted it when the packed plane missed its take-off slot in Munich and sat on the taxiway for ages. Quieter than an MRI scan, but otherwise similar.

Travel agents nowadays aren't very good with continental rail timetables. You're on your own, though websites like www.seat61.com are a help. In Italy last year we enjoyed the local trains, characterful but without air conditioning, but we wanted a faster way home. The web found us a direct service from Venice to London, which turned out to be the Orient Express. It has old-fashioned air conditioning (you open the window), which suited us fine.

Are we there yet?

Being a non-flying Scotsman is OK if, like me, you've moved to England. For those who haven't, it's tough. The train from Glasgow to London takes over 4 hours (Paris to Avignon, a similar distance, takes 2 hours 45 minutes). Aberdeen to London is one of the world's great rail journeys, but seven hours of admiring the scenery is a bit much. This is why RCOG Council members from north of the border accumulate a lot of air miles. They may even earn loyalty cards, giving them access to first-class lounges. If so, they'll find this article mystifying. Airports? Free drinks and comfy armchairs? What's not to like, Jim?

And the winner is...

I keep getting e-mails about award ceremonies. Some are non-medical. The people who took us abroad this year have been named "Best Special Interest Holiday Company (Small)" at the British Travel Awards and have sent a picture. Aaww, lovely. Others are slightly medical. The British Society of Magazine Editors (BSME) is inviting applications for its next awards bash in a posh London hotel. Pity I'm no longer editing EJOG. I see the *BMJ* was once highly commended in the "Business and Professional Magazines (weekly)" section but was pipped by the *Farmers Guardian*.

If they had an award for "Best Medical CPD Magazine (quarterly)" I'd certainly nominate *TOG*. Don't laugh. Award ceremonies have an awful lot of categories (have you ever watched the Oscars all the way through?) and *TOG* is surely the leader in its field. The BSME charges only a small fee for self-nomination but those on the final shortlist have to self-fund their evening in that five-star venue in Mayfair. What would the RCOG Finance Department make of that, I wonder?

Holding back the tears

Have I ever won an award myself? Well – ahem – since you ask, there was that Church of Scotland Song Contest back in 1975. But hey, let me be the first to point out that our winning entry, *Lord Above,* was a team effort. Most of the credit must go to my partner Walter, who composed such a great tune and played the guitar so brilliantly. Still, I hope my humble lyrics helped, and perhaps mixing rhyme and theology needed a bit of divine inspiration! Seriously though, folks, Walter and I are very, very grateful that for 40 years we've been empowered to describe ourselves as "award-winning singer-songwriters".

Wiping away my tears, I must admit it's all been downhill since then. Baby Lifeline, a charity of which I'm honorary president, was shortlisted for a couple of national awards recently. Generous sponsors financed our trips to London and we got an insiders' view of the awards business. Spotlights, loud music, expensive catering, hundreds of excited people dressed to the nines and a famous face to take charge of proceedings. Much of the action consists of winners being photographed with the famous face, who knows exactly what to do when the cameras flash, and makes sure the organisers' logos are in shot. A huge TV screen shows the distant tables what's happening onstage. When your own shortlist is announced the IT system flashes up the names and a sixth sense warns you to put on the fixed smile of a gallant loser.

Team of the year

Why go through all that hassle? Well, for a charity, recognition by an award may bring more donors, which for Baby Lifeline would mean more money for equipment and training courses. And for a performer, or a chef, an award can be career-changing. But of course doctors are above this sort of thing. Or are we? I've just turned to Google and discovered – not for the first time – that I'm way out of date. "Doctor of the Year" awards appear to be all the rage in the USA, mainly (but not exclusively) recognising the unsung heroes of rural family practice, which is in need of a boost.

Large-scale medical award ceremonies came to Britain just as I was retiring. Their main aim is to recognise teams, not individuals. At the RCM Annual Midwifery Awards entry is free and sponsors get an opportunity to "gain direct exposure to the most celebrated midwives in the UK". The *BMJ* Awards began in 2009 and now describe themselves as the UK's leading medical awards programme. For sponsors, their standard award package costs £25,000. This, says the brochure on the website, buys them lots of opportunities to enhance their corporate profile, build brand awareness and reach more than 140,000 doctors nationwide – plus the chance to "network with the leading lights of UK medicine". Sponsors last year included Leo Pharmaceuticals, NICE, the GMC and the Royal College of Anaesthetists.

Bah, humbug?

The *BMJ's* panel of distinguished judges includes many well-known doctors, who I'm sure can tell style from substance in those 15-minute presentations. The aim of all these medical awards is to raise standards, encourage innovation and disseminate good practice. Who would dare to question this – by, say, inquiring about the fees paid to the famous faces or the longevity of the award-winning schemes? Only a curmudgeon. Or an ageing Scottish singer-songwriter who always tried to draw a line between his medical and showbiz activities, and who felt that only the latter needed glitzy marketing.

Reunions:
an evidence-based review

Reunions of medical graduates are increasingly being promoted by our universities. Many of us attend. We enjoy chatting to members of our year and cheerfully pick up the flyers asking us to donate to our alma mater. Others have a deep-seated aversion to such events. It has nothing to do with targeted fundraising: they just don't see the point. A third group are undecided. They weigh the pros and cons. Is it worth the hassle? Will it repay the financial and emotional investment? When clinicians are in equipoise they should review the evidence – or have someone do it for them. Who better than a retired professor with library access? I'm happy to oblige.

First, the bad news. There are no randomised controlled trials on this topic. However, using "reunion" as a search term in Pubmed I retrieved a gratifying haul of references (n=3111). These covered a variety of subjects ranging from tropical diseases on the island of Réunion to the management of fractures. Most of them I discarded as irrelevant. The few remaining reports were highly subjective and lacked statistical rigour but form the basis of this review. For pragmatic reasons, it is restricted to general medical journals published in the UK.

Historical background

A search of the *Lancet* yielded 1,062 results, of which only 57 were from the present century. Most of the relevant reports appeared between 1880 and 1910. At that time each London teaching hospital held an annual dinner presided over by a distinguished alumnus, usually a medical knight. This all-male affair in a posh restaurant was attended by around 100 past and current students and often included an in-house revue. A detailed report with a list of toasts and proposers was published in the Lancet, announcing that a good time had been had by all. These gatherings helped foster the fierce institutional pride that once characterised London medical graduates – and is exactly what today's universities are trying to re-create.

They didn't last. In 1931 the Lancet reported that many annual reunions had been abandoned "and others are held in a form so modified as to spread gloom rather than cheer". By contrast, the dinner of the Royal Free Hospital School of Medicine for Women "stood out as a joyous function", with over 400 past and present students assembled at the Savoy Hotel. The Lancet approved of the humour and brevity of the speeches before the dancing began. Evidently medicine's gender change was gathering pace and producing a breath of fresh air.

The present day

In the past 25 years there has been only one relevant *Lancet* article. Over the same period the BMJ had 113 references to "reunion", of which 39 were in the obituary columns. Crikey: I hadn't realised they were so dangerous. Clearly reunion organisers should take precautions, such as rehearsing the Heimlich manoeuvre and limiting the Scottish country dancing. But maybe there's another explanation. It's quite likely that the *BMJ* obituarist's most recent sighting of the deceased had been at a class reunion. In which case the lesson for all reuniters is: be nice to your classmates throughout the event, just in case they're taking notes.

Across both journals there have been only ten relevant papers since 1991. One is a "How to do it" article for organisers *(BMJ* 1991;302:282-3). Although it pre-dates the internet its advice still applies, except the bit about requesting support from drug firms: even then, it prompted a letter

199

from the Association of the British Pharmaceutical Industry pointing out that this was contrary to their code of practice. The other papers are reflections written by those attending. They vary depending on the milestone – at 20 years there's an edge of competitiveness, at 50 a touch of anxiety – but overall they're remarkably similar. Their authors were driven by curiosity, discovered that some classmates looked much older than others, and were surprised that beneath the surface everyone was just the same as they had always been.

Looking ahead

So, what have we learned from this review? Not a lot. It doesn't tell us whether reunions have a future in a world of Facebook friends and enormous class sizes. As ever, the review's conclusions depend on the reviewer's opinions. My guess is that curiosity will still motivate doctors to meet, two or more decades after graduation, and I hope authors will become more willing to admit that they enjoyed themselves. As to the format, it will be hard to improve on how the Royal Free did things in 1931, even if we can't stretch to the Savoy.

Reflecting on research

I see from the last issue of *TOG* that evidence of reflective practice is now required for appraisal and revalidation. Ten years ago this would have been good news for me. I was producing reams of reflection in various medical journals and I'd have enjoyed seeing the responsible officer's face when I staggered in with my bulging portfolio. But is there any evidence that all that writing made me a better doctor? Published views about the value of written reflection vary from enthusiasm (among educationalists) to scepticism (among general practitioners) but I don't think there's any hard evidence about its effect on patient care.

Reflection is also part of trainees' assessments now. When I was a trainee our career progression depended on research. In order to be short-listed for a consultant post you needed at least nine papers in peer-reviewed journals – or so we thought. Why nine? I've no idea, but the rumour certainly frightened us into working hard. Not that we believed our research CV correlated with our performance as doctors. If anything we thought the opposite, which is why I wanted a surgical fellowship as well as an MD. If I got an interview I could always apologise for one or the other.

Junior fellow

So, was my research useful? Certainly my nine papers earned me a consultant interview, but there was more to it than that. Doing research helped me understand the strengths and weaknesses of the medical literature. That's a useful skill for a doctor even today, when guideline committees are keen to do our reading for us. Another important lesson was that researchers need to care deeply about their work – I'm trying to avoid the vogue word "passionate", which suggests a lack of objectivity. During my time as an MRC Junior Research Fellow I was surrounded by friendly people motivated by a straightforward desire to find things out. It made a refreshing change from the hospital rat race.

But was it useful to anyone other than me? Well, we did make some contributions to scientific knowledge but I wish they had been bigger. On reflection I think my MD project was ahead of its time. In 1974 my far-sighted supervisor suggested I study the human mammary gland. The first thing I discovered was that nobody else takes normal breasts seriously. Our paper on cyclical changes in breast size inspired a sackful of reprint requests and a tsunami of hilarity. Our subsequent papers, on how ovarian hormones affect mammary epithelium, were ignored. They're still occasionally cited when someone rediscovers that a woman's breast cancer risk is directly related to her lifetime number of menstrual cycles, but we still don't know enough about cell biology to understand why. When we do, those old papers are unlikely to resurface: only historians check journals from the last century.

My, how you've grown

Back then, much of my project involved collecting specimens and looking down a lonely microscope, but the best bits were when I worked alongside real scientists. Nowadays collaboration is recognised as essential and research networks are global. At our medical school's inaugural lectures, each new professor needs a very big screen to acknowledge his or her team. Their output of papers is measured in hundreds and their research grants amount to millions of pounds – thanks in some cases to those dramatic TV commercials that play on the public's fear of cancer and heart disease. Our newly appointed professors, however, represent the elite. The 5,634 journals indexed by Medline also publish a lot of stuff by authors who are content with quantity rather than quality when it comes to publications. I particularly dislike the epidemiological fishing trips which study hundreds of variables in the hope that some will turn out to be statistically significant. Does burnt toast give you cancer? Do avocados prevent miscarriages? I'm glad I'm no longer a College media spokesman.

Welcome, UKARCOG

What triggered these reflections was the first publication of UKARCOG, the UK Audit and Research trainee Collaborative in Obstetrics and Gynaecology (Risk Manag Healthc Policy 2017;10:1-6). How exciting to see a nationwide network of trainees addressing a clinically relevant topic – in this case postpartum haemorrhage. The 197 collaborators are listed at the end of the paper (charmingly, in alphabetical order of their first names). I do hope their enthusiasm will spread to the three regions (all in the south, incidentally) who haven't joined in yet. One thing puzzles me, though. Why isn't the "t" included in UKARCOG's acronym? The trainee involvement is a major strength and augurs well for the future. Something to reflect on, perhaps?

Obstetricians' statues

Does England have any statues of obstetricians? Indeed, are there any in the British Isles (apart from Edinburgh, where Simpson has been gazing across Princes Street since 1877)? If there are, I don't know about them and neither does Google. Even in Dublin, a city celebrated for obstetrics and statues, Bartholomew Mosse has no plinth outside the Rotunda Hospital, which he founded. Presumably he shares Sir Christopher Wren's epitaph: *Si monumentum requiris, circumspice* ("If you seek his monument, look around").

In general, medical heroes receive nothing more than a blue plaque, though there are exceptions. In London a bust of Joseph Lister overlooks Portland Place and there are busts of John Hunter in Lincoln's Inn Fields and at St George's Hospital. They were general surgeons. As for physicians, Edward Jenner has been sitting in Kensington Gardens since 1862 but if you're looking for public statues of William Harvey they're out of town – one in Cambridge, where he studied, and two in Kent, where he was born.

Why bother?

For obstetric statues you must travel even further afield. The finest, surely, is of Ignaz Semmelweis in his home city, Budapest. There he stands, facing his old hospital, with babies at his feet and a breast-feeding mother looking up at him, all done in marble in 1904 by Hungary's leading sculptor. In Vienna, however, where he first pioneered hand-washing, the Semmelweis Frauenklinik has a magnificent statue of Kaiser Franz Joseph I, erected in1910, upstaging the bust of Semmelweis added belatedly in 1944.

What lies behind all that expensive sculpting? National pride must be a major driver but it's not the only one. The size of Semmelweis's memorial in Budapest suggests a need to atone for the scorn heaped on him during his lifetime. He died in 1865, having introduced prophylactic hand-washing in 1847, and it was only in 1879 that Pasteur isolated the streptococcus, showing he had been right all along. To this day, people become indignant on his behalf and seem to feel that if doctors had taken him seriously they could have put an early end to puerperal fever.

Not so. Semmelweis reduced the death rate in medical wards in Vienna and Budapest but sepsis remained a leading global cause of maternal mortality until the first sulphonamide appeared in 1935. It was created by Gerhard Domagk, working for Bayer Laboratories in Wuppertal, Germany. By the time he received his Nobel Prize in 1947, nobody was putting up statues to Germans, even to one who had saved countless lives. In 2013, Bayer AG presented a sculpture entitled "Domagk" to Wuppertal.

It's an abstract by Sir Anthony Cragg, who says it symbolizes a researcher struggling to discover something.

Times change

Realistic statues provoke more powerful emotions than abstract ones, as demonstrated by people's urge to destroy them. From Ozymandias to Saddam Hussein, tyrants have left enduring images of broken statues. The imperialist Cecil Rhodes may linger in Oxford but he has been deposed from the University of Cape Town. And in the USA, controversy rages about J Marion Sims, the "father of modern gynecology". His 2.7 metre statue, cast in bronze in 1892, has stood in New York's Central Park since 1934 on a pedestal stating that he "carried the fame of American surgery throughout the entire world." National pride, however, is now giving way to concern that his first patients were slaves, unable to withhold consent, and I suspect its days are numbered. Actually, quite a lot of early gynaecological surgery makes us cringe nowadays.

Ideas, please

In these egalitarian times statues are still being erected but plinths are out of fashion, except for footballing legends outside their home grounds. Celebrities are placed life-size on the pavement – where, to be honest, they look faintly ridiculous. Nobody is going to campaign to have them pulled down: they're more likely to be accidentally knocked over. To look impressive, a ground-level statue needs a remarkably skilful sculptor – someone like Martin Jennings, whose John Betjeman in St Pancras Station is my personal favourite.

Should we approach Mr Jennings about a statue for the College's new home, wherever that turns out to be? And whom should it portray? Hmm. A male statue would be unacceptable, so it can't be a founding father or a hero like Patrick Steptoe. But choosing our first female president would smack of tokenism, and an abstract sculpture entitled "Motherhood" might attract graffiti about apple pie. No, it has to be our current president, leading us out of Regent's Park. Or if she can't be persuaded, a nice vase of flowers.

Trash or treasure?

I've just been appointed librarian to York Medical Society. "Wow," I hear you say, "what a responsibility!" Yes, indeed. For my generation, librarians are awesome figures. When we were children they were the grown-ups who lent you books, wielded a rubber stamp (a symbol of authority) and fined you a penny if they were late back. When I was a student, the medical school librarian wore a white coat (another symbol) and knew where the most sought-after textbooks were in the run-up to exams. And today, whatever your age or status, a librarian is entitled to give you a meaningful stare and tell you to shush.

Hungry for education

So you can see why I wanted the post, but why York? After all, I'm a member of the Leeds Medico-Chirurgical Society. Well, many years ago Leeds Med-Chi gave its books to Leeds University to be professionally cherished and now meets in a splendid – but sadly book-free – dining room on campus. In York, by contrast, the Medical Society has its own premises, a quiet oasis amid the city centre's buskers, in a building dating from 1590. There is a library, added in 1804, which predates the Society, founded in 1832.

York is one of a handful of medical societies which describe themselves as 'among the oldest in the country'. Their claims were examined by a Norwich physician, Dr Batty Shaw, who carefully distinguished between dining clubs and scientific societies (Med Hist 1968;12:232–44). The oldest of the latter group – at least in the English provinces – are Colchester (founded in 1774) and Plymouth (1794). Both are still going strong. Of the few purely obstetrical societies the oldest is Edinburgh's, founded in 1840. Presenting at its Registrars' Meeting in the 1970s was a terrifying experience. I'm sure the speakers at today's Junior Members Meeting are more poised than I was.

Most medical societies were founded by young(ish) doctors who wanted to improve medical care, and many began as book clubs. But books soon became more affordable and by the late 20th century Continuing Medical Education was being organised nationally. The need for local medical societies faded and the wheel has turned full circle. Many seem like dining clubs again, which makes them unattractive to busy young doctors. It takes years of experience to realise that you can learn more at a dinner than at a lecture.

Online versus paper

Who needs libraries anyway, in this internet age? Actually, historians are one group and students are another. Leeds University recently opened a new undergraduate library, a palatial building with a Caffè Nero coffee house, rooms for discussion groups, floor after floor of silent areas for laptops and, I was surprised to find, books galore. Across the campus my old stamping-ground, the medical library, now provides a large area for laptop users but – hey! – the shelves are still there, piled with prescribed textbooks. In both places the staff told me that students prefer real books at exam time, and want to read them in the library.

What has disappeared from the medical library are the long rows of bound journals, now available online. This is the opposite of what we predicted in 1999, when we cleared the old books out of our departmental library to make room for the most recent journals. That literary parting distressed me, though I tried to sound cheerful when I wrote about it in *TOG* volume 1, issue 2. How long ago it seems now. A hospital with an academic department! A department with its own library! People will ask if I made it all up.

Decisions, decisions

In preparation for my new role I've been doing some background reading. The most recent article I could find (from the *BMJ* of 1966) said: "the most difficult and time consuming task that confronts the non-professional librarian" is cataloguing. No worries – I'm happy to keep in touch with my obsessive-compulsive side. It also said: "a library's main problem is lost books and journals". Ah, things have changed. The modern medical library's biggest headache is not losing books but receiving too many, from retired doctors like me.

Offering York Medical Society my own library was what got me this new job. Now it will be up to me to decide what to accept and what to discard. It's 1999 all over again, only harder. I could form a committee but would anyone turn up? What I need are guidelines but there don't seem to be any. I may have to write them myself. Librarians of the future, watch this space.

Patrons of the arts

When you retire, the contents of your wallet change. The swipe cards for the car park, office, labour ward and business class lounge disappear. In their place come non-electronic cards stating that you're a member of the National Trust, a Friend of various theatre companies and art galleries, and a keen birdwatcher. You feel quietly proud, knowing that if the emergency services ever have to search for your Allergy Alert or organ donor card, they'll understand that they're dealing with a really cultured person.

Being a Friend of an arts organisation gives you discounts in the cafeteria and a place near the head of the ticket queue, but along with rights come responsibilities. You feel obliged to turn up at their exhibitions and actually go to their plays. And then there are the appeals for help when government grants fail to keep up with costs. As you reluctantly click 'DONATE', you realise that you've become a patron of the arts.

A wee touch of philanthropy

Doctors have a long tradition of supporting creative people – or so I thought. In Renaissance Italy, Michaelangelo's finest work was done for a family whose name, Medici, means 'doctors'. When I checked my facts, however, I discovered that by the 12th century the family had abandoned medicine for management. Once they became Florence's leading bankers they were better placed to assist struggling young sculptors. Today, it's still only the super-rich who can provide extensions to the National Gallery or have performing spaces named after them, but the rest of us can do our bit. My monthly direct debit to Opera North is for a lot less than our gas bill but it does result in an occasional letter of thanks, which is more than I get from utility companies. And signing the Gift Aid form, even for my modest contribution, has had a gratifying effect on my tax assessment. For a Scotsman like me, that's important.

Long live the king

What's this, Professor? Discussing your personal finances? That's not what we expect on the back page. Yes, sorry, but please bear with me. Like all opera lovers I'm sensitive about accusations of elitism, so I've been comparing our prices with those at the Leeds Arena. At Opera North you can enjoy the current *Madama Butterfly* for £15, going up to £72.50 in the dress circle. At the Arena, tonight's tickets for The Killers (apparently "the most successful rock band ever to emerge from the state of Nevada") start at £45, rising to £149 for the Laurent Perrier experience ("free glass of bubbly on arrival").

In my day, rock fans wouldn't have known about Laurent Perrier (Who's he, mate? One of the French impressionists?), but clearly things have changed. The Arena (capacity 13,500) is sold out for The Killers, so their gig should rake in about £1 million when you include the merchandising. Rock concerts are profitable, but are they art? They depend so heavily on lighting effects and amplifiers that I used to wonder whether live musicians were really necessary. Now I know the answer: one of next week's concerts is by Elvis Presley.

Big woolly jumpers

The joys of being a patron include helping artists early in their careers. Chatting to young singers – or indeed older actors – reminds you how hard they work for meagre rewards and how uncertain their job prospects are. They're modest about their value to society compared to doctors but I'm not sure that I still agree with them on that. Part of their job involves going into deprived communities and getting children to play music and perform. This results not only in inspirational concerts but more importantly in better exam grades across the whole school. And on a grander scale, Hull's year as UK City of Culture has gained the city national respect.

Another pleasure is attending events outside your comfort zone. When the Hepworth opened in Wakefield in 2011 my wife and I became its Friends, thinking a new gallery of modern art in Yorkshire would need all the support it could get. Last year, just before it beat London's Tate Gallery to become Art Fund Museum of the Year, I was surprised to find myself being stimulated by an exhibition of women's clothes, including giant woolly jumpers. It was curated by J.W. Anderson, a fashion designer I'd never heard of, but who, like The Killers, is famous to those in the know. This patron thing is a bit of an eye opener. It's a long way from medicine but I find it therapeutic.

Lecturers and orators

After 40 years of lecturing, I recently had a new experience. Last June I gave a talk without visual aids. That was a novelty in itself, but the real revelation came at the end of the year when I gave it again, this time with PowerPoint. I suddenly realised how wide the gulf had become between speaking and lecturing.

June's talk was to Leeds Luncheon Club, which provides speakers with a lectern, a mike, a male audience from all walks of life, but no projector. My subject was how IVF had been the brainchild of Robert Edwards, a proud Yorkshireman. I had met him a few times but I needed to do a lot of background reading, and I was delighted to discover the historical research of Martin Johnson, a former member of his team (Reprod Biomed Online 2011;23:245–62). All I had to do was summarise it and add some basic reproductive biology. Explaining the latter without diagrams, however, would require a lot of arm waving and I spent ages practising my gestures and editing the accompanying words.

The big-screen experience

The second talk was to adults of both sexes in a school hall with full audio-visual facilities. What a relief! I could revert to my routine of turning up with a memory stick and one sheet of paper. Google images produced photos of Louise Brown, Patrick Steptoe, Edwards himself, his various laboratories and finally, his wife Ruth receiving his Nobel Prize from the King of Sweden. I drove to Batley to photograph his childhood home (a modest terraced house, still without a blue plaque). He was one of nine Yorkshire-born Nobel Laureates and I made a slide of their names, dates and birthplaces. Playing with PowerPoint is much more fun than writing a script. You get so involved with the pictures that you can forget about the words.

When I spoke in that well-equipped school hall, however, I began to feel that my slides were getting in the way. In the Luncheon Club I had enjoyed the new experience of looking my fellow-diners in the eye. Now I was back in the world of medical lecturing, where we focus on something else. We used to write on a blackboard or stare at our slides. Now we talk to our laptops as the screen behind us fills with guidelines, algorithms, graphs, clip art, forest plots with unreadable labels, mini-movies (sometimes they actually move) and the logo of the institution where we work. Our words are little more than a voiceover to the visual spectacle.

Friends, Romans . . .

So much the better, you may say: a picture is worth a thousand words. Well, I don't like to quibble but when I started lecturing years ago the rule was 'one slide per minute', which means a picture is worth 150 words at normal talking speed. It's worth less than that when the slides come thick and fast, and much less when each slide is packed with too much information. But of course I still like looking at pictures. What I'm saying is that we should pay more attention to words.

My feeling was reinforced a few weeks ago when I read one of my Christmas presents, coincidentally a book about oratory. *When They Go Low, We Go High,* by Philip Collins, gives examples of speeches that have changed the world, beginning with Marcus Tullius Cicero in 44 BC. Cicero, still regarded as the master of public speaking, described various styles of oratory, ranging from the 'plain', used for teaching, to the 'grand', for arousing the emotions. I now realise that I've always used the plain style, partly because it's the language of science but also because grandiloquence was endlessly mocked by satirists during my formative years in the 1950s and 1960s. For my generation it has remained out of fashion ever since.

I have a dream

With hindsight, I think that's a shame. I wish I'd studied classical rhetoric rather than making fun of it. The job of a teacher is to inspire as well as to explain, and one of our roles as obstetricians and gynaecologists is to act as advocates for women. Sometimes we need to persuade, and that is what rhetoric is all about. I'm not suggesting that a lecture on pelvic floor anatomy should become the Gettysburg Address, but I am resolved that next time I give a talk I'll try harder to keep my slides under control and think more about what I'm actually going to say. Who knows, I might even wave my arms around.

History, fiction and Sir Lancelot

During my first week as an undergraduate, we were given a booklet about the history of our medical school. I recently began to wonder if such things still exist or if there are now electronic versions, so I conducted a telephone survey of randomly selected UK medical schools (n=2). Both had no equivalent of the booklet I received, although the students' introductory week at one includes a lecture on local medical history.

The question had occurred to me because Leeds NHS Trust has decided to celebrate the 250th anniversary of the General Infirmary by creating a historical archive and inviting each specialty to contribute. Fledgling specialties like hand transplantation can probably tell their story concisely, but maternity goes back a long way and I had to ask for our word limit to be extended. The 19th and early 20th centuries were predictably fascinating, but I was surprised to discover how little I knew about the recent past. I found a website, Secret Leeds, on which women reminisced about a maternity unit that I never knew existed. Some of the posts mentioned babies being "poorly" after birth. I did some checking and reminded myself that in 1958, Britain's stillbirth rate was 38.5 per 1000 – ten times what it is now.

Trust me, I'm a screenwriter

How quickly we forget, but we shouldn't blame ourselves. Neuroscientists tell us that forgetting is an active process, essential for our ability to think. We need to forget stuff to make room for new stuff. We sail through life on a bow-wave of fresh information, leaving a little trough of ignorance behind us. Years later we're followed by historians, sifting through the jetsam and deciding what to keep.

Joining their number, even briefly, was a challenge. What approach should I adopt? Should I list all the facts and risk boring my readers? Or should I select interesting stories to keep them entertained? All historians have to strike their own balance, and all – myself included – have to be aware of the times in which they live. In the present era of feminisation of medicine, I made jolly sure I recorded the pioneering contributions of women even if it meant skimping on the men.

But the most influential writers are those who mix history and fiction and bring the past to life. *Call the Midwife* has given the nation the definitive picture of maternity care half a century ago, though the author, Jennifer Worth, worked as a midwife for only 2 years after qualifying in 1959 and wrote her memoir 40 years later. The television adaptation in 2012 was tailored to today's audience and, I'm told, portrayed post-war midwives sympathetically.

Pantomime villain

Doctors of that period haven't been so lucky. Most of its medical fiction was written by doctors who also left their profession early but justified their career change by focusing on their former colleagues' faults. This goes down well with today's audiences, who like to think that previous generations of doctors were not as clever or as caring as the current one.

Medical educationalists, for example, still illustrate their talks with a YouTube clip from the 1954 movie *Doctor in the House* (the bit where 'Sir Lancelot Spratt' is being beastly to students on a ward round; they never show the one where he saves the students from expulsion by the humourless Dean of the Medical School). The real 'Sir Lancelot' was a charismatic surgeon who had endured the Blitz and enjoyed universal respect. For educationalists, however, he became a pantomime villain whose name is routinely used to mock generations of consultants.

I wonder why medicine, alone among the professions, has given up on learning from its past? We can pick up useful lessons about the art of medical practice from browsing the online archives of our journals, or just by Googling 'Sir William Osler', but that isn't part of the students' curriculum unless they're doing a special module on the history of medicine.

Ah, I get it!

Among my souvenirs is a letter from Richard Gordon, author of the novel *Doctor in the House*, thanking me for pointing out in an article that the films were a travesty of his book. He had a subtle sense of humour and I've just realised that the name "Lancelot" had nothing to do with King Arthur. It was perfect for a surgeon who spent a lot of time lancing abscesses. It's taken me 60 years to see the joke but gosh, that's pretty quick for someone who used to be a medical educator.

Waving on the Rhine

Last spring I visited Dusseldorf for the first time. We were a small group of gynaecologists, members of a visiting society formed in the 1970s when senior registrars organised their own continuing personal development. For us, the phrase 'lifelong learning' is no empty cliche. In our retirement our thirst for knowledge led us into an unfamiliar Krankenhaus, where the postgraduate centre was – as in the UK – impossible to find. Aha! There it is, hidden behind startled diners in the Kantine.

Why Dusseldorf? Well, why not? The reason was not just that one of our number had family there. We still like discovering places we've never seen – particularly if they're within range of budget flights from our local airport. For my generation, though, there's a downside to flying into Germany. When you're over the Ruhr you can't help thinking about The Dam Busters, however hard you try not to.

Learning from Germans

Our hosts gave talks in English and so did we. Mine was about Patrick Steptoe. In my copy of his ground-breaking book *Laparoscopy in Gynaecology*, I'd noticed that the other name on the title page is Hans Frangenheim of Wuppertal (near Dusseldorf), author of the chapter on infertility. Steptoe's chapters point out that laparoscopy began in Germany with experiments in Hamburg in 1901, that the first paper on human laparoscopy appeared in a German journal (*Jacobaeus H.M€unch med Wschr* 1910;57:2090–2), and that the first textbook on the subject was published in German by Dr Frangenheim in 1959. Steptoe visited him and Raoul Palmer of Paris and chose the German term laparoskopie over the French celioscopie when he brought the technique to the UK in 1967.

Until I prepared that presentation I knew very little about Germany's contributions to O&G. They are numerous. The front cover of Tom Baskett's book *On the Shoulders of Giants* (2nd edition) shows the faces of 90 people famous for advancing our specialty worldwide. Thirteen were German, ranging from Naegele, born in Dusseldorf in 1778, to Kleihauer, who died in Ulm in 2017. Tom's book, as well as making a good slide, is a fascinating resource – as is his new one, *A History of Caesarean Birth: from Maternal Death to Maternal Choice*. He has a rare gift for making history enjoyable.

213

Sprechen Sie Deutsch?

My ignorance of German achievements was due partly to the language barrier. More than a century has passed since British doctors learned German in order to study there. When the Royal College of Obstetricians and Gynaecologists was founded in 1929, about one-third of the founding Fellows had visited Germany or Austria as part of their training. That habit ended in 1914. Apart from Steptoe, hardly any gynaecologists visited in the 1960s, except a few who wanted to learn colposcopy. They helped found the British Colposcopy Group in 1972 and are named on the British Society for Colposcopy and Cervical Pathology website.

Today, UK doctors know little about medical practice across the Channel. Some European countries like to publish papers in English, but German doctors have no need to do so. German is the second most commonly used scientific language in the world. English-language journals, for their part, feel no need to reach out to them. Of the 27 members of the BJOG Editorial Board, seven are from the USA, four from China and two from mainland Europe. Two world wars have cast a long shadow over my generation. We boomers were raised on xenophobic stereotypes. No wonder our mindset is so much less international than that of the Edwardians.

For groups like ours which do visit Germany, the mantra used to be 'don't mention the war'. Nowadays it's 'don't mention Brexit', but inevitably the subject comes up, especially when chatting to multilingual taxi-drivers. When we tried to apologise for the referendum result their attitude was sympathetic. Germans understand better than anyone how easy it is for an electorate to be seduced by nationalism.

Auf wiedersehen, pet

We liked Dusseldorf, with its art galleries, high fashion and youthful Rhine-side cafe culture. Our town guide, in her open-toed sandals, had a light touch: "This is the courthouse. It's my favourite building in Dusseldorf. It's where I got my divorce". We visited the leafy suburb of Kaiserswerth, where Theodor Fliedner, a Lutheran reformer who had met Elizabeth Fry in England, established the school of nursing which inspired Florence Nightingale's first publication in 1851. When we left Kaiswerswerth on the boat for the city centre, our colleague's daughter and grandson waved goodbye from the riverbank. They were sad to say goodbye and so were we.

Popcorn and periods

As I write, the Leeds International Film Festival is in full swing. Leeds was where the world's first motion picture was shot, in 1888, by a little-known pioneer called Louis Le Prince. It showed people walking in the park near our house. Film has gone on from there to become a global art form that can get a bit intense at times. This year's festival began with a 'penetrating dysfunctional family drama' and continued in the same vein. Not my cup of tea, I'm afraid. For me, the art form peaked with *Paddington 2*.

Nonetheless, a few months ago my wife and I went to the Leeds-Bradford Odeon to see *Padman,* a Bollywood movie about menstrual hygiene. The trip was quite an adventure: we usually get lost in Bradford, and we weren't sure that the film would be shown – its global release kept being delayed to avoid clashing with *Padmaavat,* a big-budget epic set in medieval Rajasthan.

Why two films with such similar titles? *'Padma',* it turns out, is Sanskrit for 'lotus', a thing of beauty. *'Padmavati'* is the name of the legendary queen in Padmaavat. 'Padma Shri' is a prestigious award given by the Indian government to people of achievement. In 2016 it was awarded to Arunachalam Muruganatham, the inventor of a low-cost machine for making sanitary pads. *Padman* is his story. What a clever title! Without the web, I'd have missed its subtlety. (And not for the first time: it took me years to realise that the title *My Fair Lady* was a sly reference to how Cockneys pronounce 'Mayfair').

A universal taboo

We loved *Padman,* with its music, charismatic hero (named 'Laxmi' in the film) and emotional climax as Laxmi addresses UNICEF in New York – an event that really happened. It's based on a book by a best-selling female author, Twinkle Khanna, which describes the effects of the menstrual taboo in rural India. Laxmi's persistence in trying to develop affordable menstrual hygiene made him a social outcast and almost cost him his marriage. But the book and the film (which Khanna produced) have a lightness of touch and aren't preachy. Quite the reverse: the scene where Laxmi tests a prototype pad on himself while riding his bicycle is hilarious.

215

The film was a success in India but was banned in Pakistan, where the Board of Censors said it was "not acceptable yet in our society". Note the word 'yet'. How long will it take? A lifetime, if our experience in the UK is any guide. Here, the menstrual taboo meant that pads and tampons were subject to VAT from its introduction in 1973. Eventually there were protests – including one from me entitled 'Rags to riches' (BMJ 1992;304:646) – but it wasn't until 2001 that VAT was reduced from 20% to 5%, which is as low as it can go under European law. In Brussels too, politicians don't talk about periods.

The big picture

Will *Padman* change things in India? Possibly. Films have an emotional impact that can alter public attitudes. On TV the finale of Blue Planet 2, showing the effects of our detritus on marine life, produced a sea-change in our behaviour and could yet bring change to the sea. But in a country the size of India, the challenge is immense. According to a recent editorial in the Indian Journal of Health (2018:62:71-4), around a billion pads are used every month across the country. Most of them contain plastic, and India lacks the facilities to dispose of them ecologically, though government action is under way. About 60% of Indian women use reusable cloths but often have difficulty washing them and (as shown in *Padman*) have to dry them indoors.

Embarrassment about periods, though, is also universal. Years ago, speaking about menstruation to a hall full of medical students in Leicester, I unwrapped a Tampax and was surprised that the gasps came from the female students. How naive I was. These days I have a better understanding of the menstrual taboo – enough, at least, to know that only women can challenge it. But it's easy to look the other way. For example, the current discussion about girls in the UK missing school because of 'period poverty' is focussed on economics. Surely there's more to it than that.

This is getting a bit heavy, man

Sorry. You can see why I don't go to the cinema very often, when even a cheerful film like *Padman*, with its colourful dancing and happy ending, can leave me with troubled thoughts. Thank goodness they're already working on *Paddington 3*.

Learning to play again

As I type this I feel a sense of occasion, for two reasons. One is that when this issue of *TOG* appears I shall have been retired for exactly ten years. My farewell party was at the end of March 2009, when I was presented with a globe and an accordion. (I'd asked for one or the other but my secretary collected enough for both – many thanks, dear colleagues.) The globe can light up from the inside, which briefly amuses the grandchildren, but the piano accordion is more complicated. Black and heavy, it sat in a corner for several years, daring me to learn how to play it.

That's great, James!

Why had I asked for it? Well, when you approach retirement you worry about not having enough to do. With an accordion you can become a one-man band. As a child at our village Christmas party I had been awestruck when a little man, a bus driver by day, sat down and filled the hall with music. Six decades later at a Burns Supper in Edinburgh an accordionist did the same and I had the same reaction. My retirement plan suddenly clicked into place.

After all, I'd once had piano lessons so I ought to be able to master a squeeze box. How wrong I was. At first I couldn't get a sound out of it. It had some minor internal prolapse but even after its corrective surgery I still couldn't make it work. Years passed until an elderly lady at a local medical society heard about my plight and began badgering me. She gave me the email address of Harry, who runs an accordion orchestra in the Yorkshire Dales and teaches children of five and upwards "And octogenarians", she added brightly.

I've progressed through the preliminary, introductory (A and B) and primary stages and I'm now starting to include the black notes. However ghastly the noise, Harry beams at me and says, "Very good, James!". Being treated like a rather dim five-year-old is a liberating experience but the problem with the accordion is that you can't see your fingers. Everything depends on muscle memory. Fortunately, at my age this turns out to be in much better condition than my memory for names and dates. After a lifetime of little more than surgical knot-tying and using a QWERTY keyboard it's ready for something more challenging.

The R word

I had intended to fill this column with ten years of philosophical insights about retirement but I see I've already filled half the page with music. I suppose that's just as well. The "R word" is one that most working doctors prefer to avoid, so I'll limit myself to a couple of paragraphs that you can skip if you like. For me, the big lesson has been that retirement is a process, not just an event. It takes years and looking back, I wish I'd started the process earlier and perhaps delayed the event itself.

Like most of my generation I retired early after working flat out throughout my career. Three days without sleep? – no problem! Stop for lunch? – not us! It's no surprise that by age 60 we were burned out. We changed the service from trainee-delivered to consultant-delivered but we failed to consider the ageing process. Now, happily, the College is on the case, exploring ways of using retired Fellows and Members and hoping to persuade the NHS that doctors with many years' experience should still be valued in a service enmeshed in management guidelines. There – two paragraphs. That wasn't so bad, was it?

100 not out

The second reason for my sense of occasion is that this is my 100th column for *TOG* and its predecessor *The Diplomate,* first published in 1994, which metamorphosed into *TOG* five years later. So this is *TOG's* 20th birthday and the back page's silver jubilee. After 25 years I'm paranoid about repeating myself and occasionally check my early contributions. I'm surprised at their frivolousness. My career as a BMJ columnist began in 1988 and in some of those pieces it's clear that my intention was to be hilarious.

It's hard to imagine such humorous stuff being accepted now, even at Christmas. Laughter among doctors has become politically incorrect, despite its important role in relieving stress. The tide may be turning, though. For example, calls are growing for the reinstatement of the doctors' mess, where trainees can relax together in private. It's about time. Doctors have been working too hard for too long and I hope they can learn to play again.

A night at the museum

The RCOG, like many Royal Colleges, has an interesting museum but unlike others we don't make a big thing of it. In fact, for the last few years we've kept it under the stairs. Will it be housed in more splendid surroundings when we move to Union Street? I hope so. Plans are already afoot for an accessible cafe (the essential feature of any contemporary museum) so we're halfway there already.

Roll up! Roll up!

Museums are big business these days. Last year in London nearly six million people visited the British Museum, while north of the border the National Museums pipped Edinburgh Castle as Scotland's top visitor attraction. Part of their allure, I suppose, is the fact that admission is free but there's more to it than that. People can be fascinated by history if it's expertly presented, which is why so many museums, including medical ones, are having makeovers.

The Royal College of Surgeons in Lincoln's Inn Fields is undergoing massive redevelopment and when it reopens, the Hunterian Museum will occupy most of the ground floor. Meantime its collection of 50,000 specimens and instruments can be browsed online at Surgicat.rcseng.ac.uk. In Edinburgh, Surgeons Hall has recently had a £4.5 million upgrade and now houses three museums. Tourists with a taste for the macabre can see dental equipment, tumours, surgically-removed foreign bodies and a book covered by the skin of Burke the murderer. Or go on a walking tour entitled "Blood and guts".

Our past and proud of it

If the public wants blood we can provide it but I suspect this is not the image the RCOG wants to project in these sensitive times. After years of being criticised by everyone (except our patients) for doing large numbers of hysterectomies and caesarean sections we're now embarrassed by our surgical past. And even by our forceps, though they've saved the lives of countless mothers and babies over the years. We no longer conduct

219

instrumental deliveries under a blanket like the Chamberlens but neither do we unwrap the forceps with a theatrical flourish and wait for the birth partner to applaud. Or at least, not often.

Our specialty has a story of historic achievements but how to tell it? In Leeds in the 1990s I tried to help the Thackray Medical Museum illustrate the spectacular fall in UK maternal mortality during my parents' lifetime. I drew a graph which a designer expanded and filled with little clay models of pregnant tummies. The eye-catching torsos grabbed visitors' attention – so much so that they didn't notice my graph at all. Today the Thackray has closed for its own costly makeover and his models are probably on E-bay.

Museums Inc.

There's a knack to using objects to tell stories and it's not a job for amateurs. Fortunately the RCOG museum now has a professional curator. After Peter Basham moved here from the Royal College of Physicians in 2016, retired Fellows like myself slowly became aware that the museum world has moved into the 21st century. Last year the RCOG joined a network, London Museums of Health and Medicine (http://medicalmuseums.org), whose 26 members range alphabetically from the Alexander Fleming Laboratory Museum to the Worshipful Society of Apothecaries. Our nearest neighbours when we move to Southwark will be the Gordon Museum of Pathology (which is not open to the public) and the Old Operating Theatre Museum (which is).

How open do we want to be? At present the curator runs guided tours on request and the majority of the 50 or so groups each year are midwives (the RCOG now houses the Royal College of Midwives' collection). We obstetricians probably feel that we don't need to be guided around our own treasures but perhaps we should give it a try. We might learn a lot.

Hello, Dolly

Museums can inspire as well as inform. Recently I attended a gala evening at the Royal Scottish Museum, which has just completed an £80 million transformation from Victorian institution to modern tourist attraction. Wandering past Lewis chessmen and Sir Jackie Stewart's racing car I found

220

myself face to face with Dolly the Sheep, slowly rotating on a pedestal. I'd seen a sheep before, but this time the wow factor kicked in. That nose! Those eyeballs! That wool! All produced by the nucleus of a mammary cell – gee whizz! I've always been amazed that two little cells can create a baby and Dolly reignited that sense of wonder. It's the kind of feeling that can make a blasé teenager decide to study reproductive biology, or perhaps even obstetrics.

South London: a newcomer's guide

The College's departure from Regent's Park is only weeks away but many Fellows outside the M25 still don't know exactly where our new base is, and some are unhappy about moving. I'm here to help. Let me lead you through the streets of London and show you some things that may help you change your mind.

Stay close, please

Our tour starts in the City, outside Monument Station, near where the Great Fire began in 1666. We'll walk across London Bridge, built first by the Romans but later replaced. I'll go ahead holding aloft my furled umbrella. Pay attention! To our left is Tower Bridge, completed in 1894. Ahead of us is the Barrowboy and Banker, a public house dating back to 2017. It has a magnificent interior reflecting its origin as a branch of National Westminster Bank. We shall have a drink there to celebrate our achievement in crossing the Thames.

Long ago the only doctors who came south of the river were those who worked at Guy's or St Thomas' Hospitals. Guy's, founded in 1721, is in St Thomas Street, near here, its tower block dwarfed by The Shard. Its historic buildings now form a campus of King's College London. St Thomas' moved away in 1862 to make room for the viaduct leading into London Bridge Station. Its old operating theatre survives as a tourist attraction.

Medical geography

Why, you ask, did so few doctors come here? The answer lies in London's social history. In the 16th century the north bank was home to the Royal College of Physicians and the Guild of Barber-Surgeons. In the 17th and 18th centuries fashionable districts were built to the west of the City – all of them north of the river. Medical institutions like the BMA and the GMC were founded in these posh areas in the 19th century and were joined in the 20th century by the new Royal Colleges.

The south bank was always different. In Shakespeare's time it was home to theatres and brothels and later it housed the working classes. Somerset Maugham's 1894 novel *Liza of Lambeth* was set in the slums around St Thomas' where he worked as an obstetric trainee. In 1913 King's College Hospital came south to Camberwell but even in the 1980s I needed all my life skills to persuade a cabbie to take me there. Gentrification was under way, however, and today my daughter and her family live near Brixton, close to the hospital where she works as a consultant. That's why I have enough local knowledge to be your guide.

Onward and southward

Let's go on. We're already halfway to Union Street. We pass Southwark Cathedral, once St Mary Overie Priory, site of the very first St Thomas' Hospital in the 12th century. On our left is London Bridge Station, dating from 1836: its recent revamp has been shortlisted for the RIBA-Stirling Prize. We pop into Borough Market, the well-known foodie destination, then cross Southwark Road and proceed down Borough High Street past the War Memorial, a Grade II* listed building. Beyond the traffic lights is the Royal College of Occupational Therapists but we turn right and – *voila!* Our new south-facing College building! Now, it's time for your frequently-asked questions. Yes?

FAQs

Do the natives speak English?

French predominates in the play-parks of Clapham but here in Southwark people speak English – of a sort. The patois of barrow boys and bankers takes some getting used to.

Where can I park?

Nobody brings a car to London nowadays and young Londoners are giving up driving. Therefore this doesn't qualify as an FAQ. Next question, please!

How do I get here, then?

Union Street is on the Q14 Quietway cycle route and is only 400m from London Bridge Tube Station – closer than Sussex Place was to Baker Street. If by force of habit you do find yourself at Baker Street, take the Jubilee Line south but don't alight at Southwark. It's at the wrong end of Union Street. Stay on until London Bridge.

Will I miss Regent's Park?

Be honest! How often did you stroll there? Here, Guy's Campus has trees and lawns. Little Dorrit Park celebrates the area's links with Charles Dickens but it is indeed little.

Time to reflect

On our all-too-brief tour we have seen not only geography but also history – how London's hospitals moved as the population shifted, and how medicine's centre of gravity has moved too. Most importantly, we have begun to suspect that, pleasant though Georgian elegance is, it's good for a forward-looking medical college to be somewhere more vibrant.

Memories of Regent's Park

As the last removal van left Sussex Place with the presidential kettle on board, the race began among us oldsters. Which of us would be first to publish their memoirs of the College's sixty years in Regent's Park? I'll set the ball rolling but others will surely follow.

We've been inspired by last September's event marking the 40th anniversary of Steptoe and Edwards' first College lecture on IVF. Our celebrations included a recording session in which senior Fellows recalled where they sat during the lecture, how long the applause lasted and how difficult it had been to get to London in January 1979. Their stories were fascinating. Thank goodness they've now been transcribed for posterity.

Memories and beyond

First-hand memories, however, go back only so far. Who can remember the opening of the College building on 13th July 1960? Not me, but I do know what I was doing that day. I was on a school excursion to Switzerland. It was my first trip abroad, my first time in a plane, and my first ... but I digress. Sorry. On that historic date the Queen was welcomed to Regent's Park by a professor from Leeds but he was my predecessor's predecessor.

We can glimpse how it felt to be an obstetrician back then by checking the journals of the time. In July 1960 the *BMJ* noted that the UK maternal mortality rate had fallen below "0.4/1000" (40/100,000) and asked if this was the irreducible minimum. With the Abortion Act still seven years away, 22% of maternal deaths were in early pregnancy. The *BJOG* (then *The Journal of Obstetrics and Gynaecology of the British Empire*) carried a paper by Professor Norman Jeffcoate advocating diagnostic culdoscopy. Patrick Steptoe's monograph on laparoscopy was also seven years away: 1967 would be a landmark year for our specialty.

Getting personal

My personal memories of 27 Sussex Place begin with the Membership admission ceremony of July 1978. I had taken the exam in Manchester – twice. Before my second attempt I got wise and attended the Queen Charlotte's MRCOG course. I remember the feeling of relief when I passed but almost nothing of the ceremony itself, except a sense of awe. There he was – the President, Sir John Dewhurst, author of the textbook I'd tried to memorise. In the flesh! Did he shake hands with me? I'm not sure. All I remember is the wow factor.

The after-effects of that initiation never quite wore off for me or, I suspect, for others. From then on, whenever we entered the Nuffield Hall for a scientific meeting or an annual dinner, we felt a little thrill. It helped, of course, that the hall was so elegant. It was designed by Louis de Soissons, who also planned Welwyn Garden City. He came from a long line of French aristocrats and imbued the room with *je ne sais quoi*, if not *oo-la-la*. The Annual Dinners attracted medicine's great and good, drawn not by the hall but by the wine cellar, which was equally spectacular in its own way. Sir John's successor, Sir Anthony Alment, a delightful man and an oenophile, bought so shrewdly that years later the wines had become too expensive for us to drink. In Council some argued for keeping them nonetheless, but Naren (later Lord) Patel organised a blind tasting which included some plonk from a corner shop. Our verdicts were deeply embarrassing and convinced the doubters that our cellar was too good for the likes of us.

A small family business

For me the most memorable event in the Nuffield Hall was the Staff Christmas Party in 2000. There are photographs of the President (Bob Shaw) and four fellow officers (Vice-Presidents, Honorary Secretary and Honorary Treasurer) wearing silly hats and singing comic songs. Our long-serving College Secretary, Paul Barnett, starred with a colleague in a sketch that involved fishnet stockings and a lamp-post. It was all great fun and we thought we had started a new tradition. Instead, we were at the end of an era.

At that time the College still felt like family. Not only Paul but also the Mace-Bearer, the porters and many of the other staff had been there for decades. But change was coming: name badges, rooms for hire, locked administrative corridors and – good heavens! – the College was even running its own MRCOG courses. No more Queen Charlotte's or single-author textbooks or automatic knighthoods. Long before we thought of moving to Southwark the old world had gone. But the memories remain and we should write them down.

Obstetrics at the National

If you search online for "history + obstetrics", the first article that comes up may well be mine, written twenty years ago. It began as a talk for a local meeting and became a 5000-word review for the *Postgraduate Medical Journal*. I was a working professor then and felt guilty about spending so much time on it. A historical review wouldn't earn me any brownie points from my academic appraisers, who want professors to spend all their time writing grant applications. That must be why nobody has written a more recent one.

When I looked at it again recently, my mind boggled. All those facts! How on earth did I find the information, a few years BG (Before Google)? There are rows of books in my study but it's hard to remember the days when I actually had to read them. Doing so, of course, didn't make me a historian. Real scholars decipher handwritten scrolls or exhume typescripts from dusty box files. All I did was read chapters written by colleagues and combine the results of their hard work. If I'd called it "historical meta-analysis" I might have got those brownie points.

Smellie to the rescue

Why was I re-reading it? Well, I'd received an email from someone who had found it on the web. Lizzie, an assistant stage manager at the National Theatre (NT), wrote to say they were producing a new play set in Suffolk in 1759. *The Welkin* is about a woman convicted of murder who is claiming to be pregnant, which would allow her to escape the gallows. The law required a "jury of matrons" to decide whether she was telling the truth. The cast, said Lizzie, were already in rehearsal and wanted to discuss how pregnancy was diagnosed in the mid-18th century. Would I help?

How could I refuse? That would have been un-neighbourly, now that the College is almost next door. I arranged to drop in. "And by the way," said Lizzie. "The script mentions a speculum. Could you say something about that?"

After putting the phone down I soon discovered that my article said nothing about speculums or pregnancy diagnosis in 1759. But on a high shelf I had a facsimile copy of William Smellie's *Textbook of Midwifery*, dated "MDCCLII" – only seven years before the date of the play. Just the job!

Mugging up

Studying it on the train to London brought a déjà-vu feeling of swotting for my MRCOG viva. Happily, fundal height measurement hasn't changed in 260 years but I looked in vain for the word "speculum". Somewhere beyond Grantham I found it, much to my relief. According to the web the speculum was used in antiquity and reinvented in the 19th century, and I'd been worried that I would have to recommend a major rewrite   But Smellie briefly referred to a "fpeculum", so I could relax.

There was a circle of chairs in the big rehearsal room and we – playwright, director, twelve female actors (some of them famous) and myself – sat down at random. They were all charming and interested. They'd already had a talk from an expert in 18th century housework (the play begins with a stunning tableau of chores) and were expecting much from me. Sadly, I could tell them little. In the 18th century, a doctor might be involved in labour but not in early pregnancy. There was no such thing as antenatal care, though a "wise woman" might be consulted, particularly if the pregnancy was unwanted.   Women's culture was secret and nothing had been written down for the benefit of future historians.

Our predecessors' limitations had taken me aback but they were already in the script. The Welkin means "heaven" in Old English and the play made much of Halley's comet, which was predicted to appear in 1759 and sure enough, did. One of the characters says: "I do think it very queer that we know more about the movement of a comet ... than the workings of a woman's body". She might have added, "or a man's, for that matter", but this is 2020 and feminism rules.

What do you think of it so far?

When the play opened in January the critics' reaction was modified rapture. Some thought it contained too much information.   As Shakespeare showed in his big hits like *Richard III* and *Macbeth,* history plays should focus on the story, not the facts. But full marks to the NT for checking. If you're quick you can make up your own mind. *The Welkin* runs until 23rd May.

[The last sentence had been deleted when this article appeared in the April 2020 issue of *TOG*. "The Welkin" became a casualty of lockdown when the NT shut down on 28th March.]

A launch in lockdown

One of the many events that didn't happen in the spring of 2020 was the launch of my new book. It would have been a first for me and I was looking forward to it. Over the years my name has appeared on various medical texts as part of an editorial team, but they were never launched at glitzy parties. Or if they were, I wasn't invited.

This book is different. A friend suggested collecting all the columns I've written in the BMJ and, more important, he put me in touch with a publisher who liked the idea. All I had to do was obtain permission, re-type the manuscripts and resist the temptation to re-edit them. As I tapped my way through 250 or so articles – some funny, some furious – I felt a growing sense of detachment. It was like reading another person's diary. I began to ask myself: what had driven that chap to write all this stuff?

Iconic columns

The answer might be that I've always enjoyed jokey columns. In the 1950s there was Beachcomber, a *Daily Express* regular with anarchic humour that would now be labelled "pythonesque". At school I discovered Addison and Steele, who founded *The Spectator* in 1711 and created Sir Roger de Coverley, a forerunner of *Private Eye's* Sir Bufton Tufton.

They mocked in very different ways but I loved their style. As a student I blew 15p weekly on Punch, which had the comic genius of Alan Coren (father of Giles and Victoria) and Miles Kington, creator of "franglais". Both are gone but not forgotten: somewhere in Wiltshire there's a bench inscribed, "In fond memory of Miles Kington, who hated this spot." *Punch* also died – too gentlemanly for the 1990s – though English comic writing lived on through the like of Keith Waterhouse and today, Craig Brown.

But I don't think they inspired me to write. I knew I could never match them or the American greats like S.J. Perelman or Dorothy Parker. I think my urge was hereditary. Two generations back a relative used to contribute hilariously to the *Shetland Times*. My father wrote for the Clydesdale Bank's staff magazine, extracting humour from life in an Ayrshire village. Explain that, geneticists. It's hidden in a chromosome, out of reach of PCR.

Medical funny pages

Medical journals have never been big on belly-laughs but some used to provide light relief from their science and politics. From its first issue in 1953 *Obstetrics & Gynecology* had a column called *After Office Hours,* with articles like "Medicated Nursery Rhymes". Its founding editor believed that "physicians should take care to avoid becoming totally immersed in medicine". In 1939 *The Lancet*'s response to the declaration of war was to begin a column called *In England Now,* which had witty anecdotes intended to boost medical morale. More effective, even for my generation, than 2020's emotional outpourings.

Medicine's sense of humour faded at the end of the century. *After Office Hours* lasted until 2001 but *In England Now* closed in 1993. The latter's by-line, "From Our Peripatetic Correspondent", had allowed its brilliant contributors to remain anonymous, as required by medicine's unwritten code in those days. Are such amusing doctors still around? They're hard to find, according to Richard Smith, the former *BMJ* editor who kindly wrote a foreword for my book. He too believes it's important for medical journals to have a few funny articles. Thank goodness for him and his few enlightened fellow-editors, say I.

The proof is in the post

My column wasn't all funny. I tried to alternate between serious and lighthearted but when the articles are all together it's hard to tell the difference. Is it a good idea to publish them again? Humour quickly dates, as does controversy. "How to telephone a hospital" seems old-fashioned now and "Are breasts redundant organs?" might no longer cause global outrage. But my lambasting of the Home Office for its attitude to overseas doctors may still strike a chord.

In March my publisher reassured me that the book was on schedule. He's just sent me a proof copy. Thirty seconds of hand-washing and there it was, with my cheerful face on the cover. Checking for typos will pass the time in lock-down and my wife and I can start planning our on-line launch party. Champagne and selfies for two. Cheers!

Stop Press: *"This Medical Life" by James Owen Drife should now be available from bookshops, Gazelle Books or Amazon.*

Zooming into history

Lockdown has been a productive time for us over-70s. We've generated record amounts of garden waste and learned new skills. I can now count up to 100 in Welsh and play the theme from *Allo Allo* on my accordion – though not yet at the same time. And I can shop on-line. I'm awaiting delivery of new carpet slippers, mine having disintegrated from over-use. When all meetings were cancelled in March I thought my lecturing career had finally ended. It had been winding down but the habit of addressing an audience is hard to break completely. I'd joined a group of doctors trying to cope with retirement by meeting in a country pub and taking it in turns to give a talk, usually about a new book or a hobby. When the pandemic hit we stopped for a while, and then we discovered Zoom.

America on line

For us, the pleasure of lecturing doesn't come from listening to one's own voice or watching listeners trying to stay awake, but from preparing the talk. If the subject is unfamiliar you get the thrill of discovery but even better is exploring history you thought you knew already. Filling the gaps is deeply satisfying, like completing a jigsaw.

And these days it's easy. Even the most obscure papers can be accessed online. Recently I typed *Transactions of the Edinburgh Obstetrical Society1870-1939* into Google. The predictive text was understandably slow to kick in but then, magically, the journal appeared. I could visit either the University of Pennsylvania or America's PubMed and download my target paper for free. Thanks a million, folks, and God bless the USA.

Pioneers of handwashing

Reading old journals soon stops you using the recent buzz-word "unprecedented", especially in relation to epidemics. When puerperal fever swept Aberdeen in the 1790s a local doctor, Alexander Gordon, wrote: "physicians who have attended patients ... ought carefully to wash themselves and get their apparel properly fumigated before it be put on again". It's tempting to hail that as the first published guidance on PPE but it wouldn't be right. Doctors could transmit the disease from patient to patient but weren't personally at risk.

Gordon's report admitted frankly, "I myself was the means of carrying the infection to a great number of women". Today a wall plaque in Aberdeen honours him for being the first person to describe the infectious nature of childbed fever, but in 1795, when his report appeared, the citizens were not best pleased. He had to leave town and died four years later.

He was forgotten until 1875 when a London physician, Dr RJ Lee, rehabilitated him in the *BMJ*. By then hand-washing was starting to gain ground, though this had little to do with either of its now-famous pioneers. Semmelweis had conducted his ground-breaking trial in Vienna in 1847 but he, like Gordon, died in obscurity long before his reputation was restored by a fellow-Hungarian, Theodore Duka, writing in *The Lancet* in 1886.

Camera, lights, action!

I discovered these details while researching a talk for our local medical history society, cancelled but now rescheduled as my Zoom debut. I'm nervous. In the old days, if technology failed I could ditch the slides and talk more loudly. This time, alone in my attic, I'll be totally dependent on my wi-fi connection. Opening the skylight and hollering won't be an option. And what about my virtual background: which mediaeval library should I choose?

The problem with remote lecturing is the standard set by professionals – TV history presenters who deliver each bite-sized paragraph in a new location on a different continent. They don't have to struggle to make PowerPoint work. They let the drone shots speak for themselves. Worst of all, they've trained today's audience to have a short attention span. Gone are the days of Dr Lee's lecture on Alexander Gordon, reproduced verbatim across eight closely printed columns in the *BMJ*.

So how much detail should I squeeze in? When I mention Leonard Colebrook, everyone will know about his *Lancet* paper announcing that puerperal fever can be cured by Prontosil. It was a sensation in 1936 and became a classic. In 1933, however, he had published a long paper in the predecessor of the *BJOG*, showing how the disease could be prevented by hand-washing. A few years later he focussed on burns, and he and his wife campaigned successfully for mandatory guards on electric fires. He may not have become a hero of medical myth, but the reality is so much more interesting, don't you think?

And now for something completely different

One of the unnoticed casualties of the pandemic has been the formal dinner. November 2020 came and went without the black ties and expensive dresses of the College's Annual Dinner. Burns Suppers have been cancelled across the globe. Our local medical society is now using Zoom for all its meetings, including the wine tasting, but the dinner was too big a challenge. We thought of using Deliveroo but it wouldn't have been the same.

What these grand occasions offered, besides classy food and good company, was speeches. The last after-dinner speech I heard was almost a year ago and I was the one giving it. My speaking engagements have been dropping off ever since I retired but this is the first time I've gone a whole year without one. I'm worried about becoming deskilled.

How (not) to do it

Medical after-dinner speaking is a craft that needs constant practice. You keep learning by experience. Or, to put it bluntly, you keep making mistakes. The worst of those – and the easiest to avoid – is failing to do your homework. Years ago at the RCOG Annual Dinner the guest speaker (a famous author) kept referring to us as a "club". He wasn't being satirical: he simply hadn't bothered to find out who we were. We took it badly.

Any speech must be tailored to the occasion and this is particularly important if you're trying to be funny. That's why touring stand-ups always start with, "Hello, Leeds!" (or wherever) and some local jokes. Crucially, though, your geography needs to be accurate. Years ago, in front of a distinguished audience in Liverpool, I name-checked another well-known seaport. They were shocked, but not as much as I was. *Memo to self: concentrate!*

During fifty-odd years of speaking I've learned many lessons the hard way. One is that the speech must be literally "after dinner". Long ago an organiser, trying to be kind, suggested I speak before the meal so that I (and he) could relax and enjoy the evening. The faces of those hungry doctors in Harrogate haunted me for years afterwards. I think of them every time I drive past the Majestic Hotel.

But you can have good times too. Giving an after-dinner speech is like going on a blind date. Sometimes you and the audience click from the start and have a great evening together. Other times the relationship needs work but you can still part as friends. Just make sure they can hear and see you, and remember the old surgical aphorism: if in doubt, cut it out. No audience ever complained that a speech was too short.

Learning to laugh again

If it's unpredictable and so much trouble, why do it? Well, you get a buzz when it goes well. And you feel sorry for the dinner organiser, who may have been traumatised by discovering what it costs to hire a professional. According to one website, speakers' fees range from £ to £££££. Even £ is too much for a small society and if they could afford an eye-watering fee, do doctors want to hear an ageing sportsperson or (heaven help us) a motivational speaker?

For me, the main reason for doing it is that it's worthwhile. Laughter bonds people together and doctors rarely get the chance to laugh these days. We're seen – and we see ourselves – as authority figures, and laughter is subversive. Royal Colleges take themselves extremely seriously and daren't risk humour at their dinners. It's increasingly likely that someone with a mobile phone will take offence and tweet.

Nevertheless there are still a few of us who believe it's our duty to navigate this minefield. Doctors deserve a chance to relax and enjoy themselves. What's more, as we've learned over the past year, we need it.

From stand-up to sit-down

Which is why I've agreed to give a virtual after-dinner speech at a Zoom conference next week. The dinner on Thursday evening has of course been cancelled but the speech has been moved to 3.30pm on the Friday, just before people wave goodbye.

Yes, I know. This will be the Majestic Hotel all over again. But I'll give it my best shot. I'll forget all my experience and start from scratch – hence the title above. *Memo to self: it's from the 1970s! Change it.* I'll need a new role model from the small screen – Clive James perhaps, or someone who's still alive. Could it possibly work? And with the audience on mute, how will I find out?

Doctors and authors

Another lockdown, another unexpected addition to my CV. Our local medical society has appointed me Honorary Online Quizmaster. Zoom is ideal for picture questions but how local should they be? And how medical? I've steered clear of *Name that rash* but included some of Yorkshire's lesser known castles snapped from unusual angles.

One of the rounds is *Medical authors.* Sir Arthur Conan Doyle should be easy to recognise with his big moustache but Anton Chekhov might be more of a challenge and AJ Cronin will probably flummox everyone. All three were proper authors. The word originally meant "creator" and they dreamed up Sherlock Holmes, Uncle Vanya and Doctor Finlay respectively. There are no bonus points for knowing that.

Fighting the urge

All three were also proper doctors. Chekhov continued to practise after becoming a literary celebrity. Medicine, he said, was his wife and literature his mistress. Conan Doyle published his first story as a student in Edinburgh but went on to graduate and even wrote an MD thesis. He practised in Portsmouth and then London, but after Holmes and Watson hit the big-time in the *Strand Magazine* in 1891 he became a full-time writer. Cronin, a Glasgow graduate, was a GP in South Wales, achieved an MD and MRCP and also moved to London. His first novel was a huge success and he too gave up medicine – but not completely. His third novel exposed the health problems of Welsh miners and his fourth, *The Citadel,* attacked greed and charlatanism in Harley Street. It caused a sensation and is credited with helping to create the climate of opinion that led to the NHS. Becoming rich and famous is an understandable reason for abandoning a medical career but some would-be authors quit before writing a bestseller. They decide that medicine is incompatible with the creative urge, which the journalist HL Mencken described as "an over-powering impulse to gyrate before one's fellow men, flapping one's wings and emitting defiant yells." This is not explicitly forbidden by GMC guidelines but it doesn't go down well at team meetings.

Their first novel will almost certainly be set in a hospital and feature a sensitive junior doctor being traumatised by the realities of medicine and by heartless consultants. The book-buying public is a sucker for angst and today's authors, like their Victorian predecessors, lay it on with a trowel. Their skill is to make it believable and they sometimes create images that last forever. Harley Street still hasn't recovered from Cronin's assault.

Fact versus fiction

Consultants have been depicted as fictional baddies for as long as I can remember. Richard Gordon's subtly affectionate portrait of Sir Lancelot Spratt appeared in *Doctor in the House* in 1952. John Rowan Wilson's far from affectionate description of the senior staff at Leeds General Infirmary came three years later in *The Pack*. Both books were made into films and influenced the public's view of senior doctors. Today's consultants no longer turn up in chauffeur-driven Rolls-Royces but "Sir Lancelot" is still a term of abuse.

Wilson and Gordon left medicine early but other successful authors stuck at it. Colin Douglas skewered Edinburgh Royal Infirmary with *The Houseman's Tale* in 1976 but the only doctors he upset were the ones he left out. He stayed and became a respected geriatrician. In the USA Samuel Shem's *The House of God* did a similar hatchet job on Boston's Beth Israel Hospital in 1978. He continued in psychiatry but moved to New York.

They belong to the small minority of consultant authors who write fiction. The rest of us stick to facts, which – let's face it – are more interesting. Writing textbooks and papers demands clarity and this can be hard work. "Good prose is like a window pane", wrote George Orwell, and we try to achieve invisibility.

Look back in humour

When we retire, however, we consider flapping our wings and writing our memoirs. Most of us don't, telling ourselves they'll interest only friends and family, but there are exceptions. Tom Baskett, author of *Names and Eponyms in Obstetrics and Gynaecology* (*TOG* 2019; 21: 220) has just published *The dog comes with the practice* – funny and moving stories from his days as a young obstetrician, first in Belfast during the Troubles and then in the Canadian Arctic. No angst here. Tom enjoyed his work and had a warm relationship with patients, midwives and colleagues. His book has something to say to today's trainees. If you're tired of "misery lit", read this and feel better.

Golden jubilee

Yes, it's fifty years since I graduated. As I write, the class of 1971 is waiting to hear if our long-planned reunion can go ahead. Cancellations and postponements have become a way of life recently but we're keeping our fingers crossed. This is the big one – psychologically and literally. The class of 1970 were forced to call off their reunion last year and after some high-level negotiations we've agreed that they can join ours. This could be the bonanza that Edinburgh's hospitality industry has been waiting for.

Why celebrate?

That's a good question, frequently asked by killjoys. Celebrating is a basic instinct with a long history. Silver and diamond anniversaries were Victorian inventions but golden jubilees are as old as time. They were prescribed in the *Old Testament*, as I'm sure you know. Chapter 25 of the book of *Leviticus* states that one year in every seven will be a sabbatical and after seven sabbaticals we get an extra year off. That special fiftieth year has to be proclaimed by the sound of trumpets, which in Biblical times were ram's horns. In fact, the word "jubilee" is derived from the Hebrew word for "ram". (Don't you just love the online *Oxford English Dictionary?*)

Music and laughter

As it happens, the sound of trumpets is already part of our planned programme. Our undergraduate band is set to have one last blow for old time's sake. There will be poignant gaps in the line-up but the sousaphone will be there to cheer people up. Our tailor-made Beatles arrangements were just the thing for May Balls in the groovy sixties and the edgy seventies, and we hope they'll still sound good when people are actually listening. This time health and safety considerations will discourage our classmates from twisting, bopping or pogo-sticking. It will be a concert performance and the band will feel the pressure.

The humorous entertainment will be even more demanding. What on earth made us agree to resurrect our student revue? Dusting off those old scripts was a heart-sink experience. That sketch about the green-eyed yellow idol to the north of Kathmandu is culturally insensitive on all sorts of levels. Like popular music, styles of humour change with bewildering speed over the years, but that's where the similarity ends. Old tunes make you smile. Old jokes make you cringe.

And new jokes are a challenge for us septuagenarians. I remember our much-loved professor of anatomy, an expert on neuronal pathways, telling us that the pineal gland is thought to be the site of the sense of humour because it calcifies in middle age. Time has proved him right but happily the brain's music centre doesn't atrophy and our stock-in-trade has always been comic songs. We considered creating *Lockdown - the musical* but a Google check revealed that this title has been grabbed by a school in Essex. No problem – we'll revert to parodies. Jools Holland's catchy theme tune *"Enjoy Yourself (It's Later Than You Think)"* will be updated to *"Unmute Yourself (It's Easier Than You Think")* for our rousing singalong ending.

The Covid effect

Speaking of Zoom, thank goodness nobody has suggested an online reunion. That's a relief but not a surprise. Facebook has been around for seventeen years without denting people's appetite for meeting face to face. There is such a thing as a reunion app but it can't cope with hundreds of people. Nor can Zoom allow everyone to talk at once.

What we would need is some version of the dating app "Tinder" which (they tell me) allows you to see lots of people and swipe left for those you want to avoid. At first sight that seems ideal for class reunions but there could be problems. Did they say left or right? And if it is left, would swiping right count as sexual harassment? And what happens if by mistake you're holding your mobile upside down? No, it has to be reality or nothing..

If the reunion does go ahead it will be our first mass gathering for over a year. There's no knowing what effect that might have on us. Edinburgh graduates of a certain age don't do hugging, let alone whooping, but we might find ourselves overwhelmed by the sense of release. It could be graduation night all over again, or like those old black-and-white films of VE Day. A socially-distanced conga along Princes Street? Scenes of debauchery on Arthur's Seat (weather permitting)? We can but hope.

Our next book

This page is having bad luck with its predictions. The class reunion I was looking forward to in the July issue has been postponed to 2022 and my comment in April that "most of us don't write our memoirs" is turning out to be premature. At the end of 2020 I decided to write a book on the history of the Confidential Enquiries into Maternal Deaths (CEMD). I've got as far as 1988 when I joined the national team of assessors. From here on, history will overlap with memoir. I'll be mentioning people I knew personally or revered as teachers and it will be hard to be objective. Perhaps the book will be more interesting if I don't try.

The target readership

I've asked colleagues to help but what should we call it? With an inspired name it could be a best-seller. Tolstoy's *All's Well that Ends Well* became a classic after he called it *War and Peace*. Luckily one of my co-authors has a flair for titles. When Gwyneth Lewis became Director of the CEMD in 1990 she re-named the reports *Why Mothers Die* and then *Saving Mothers' Lives*. We think some combination of the two might do the trick.

The book will be aimed at "the well-informed lay person". This will involve writing readable prose but we think it's important to make the effort. It's high time the public was told how much work was needed to make childbirth safe in the UK. The more you discover about how the CEMD began, the more you're awestruck by the people who made it happen. Your first reaction is, "Gosh! They could never have done that today" but I'm not so sure. Our predecessors faced the same political barriers as we do but they had the skills and guile to overcome them. It's a shame that their names are forgotten.

But it won't be easy to turn them into heroes. What modern readers want are stories about mavericks battling the establishment. The CEMD, however, was set up by the president of the RCOG and a senior civil servant, both of whom received knighthoods. We'll focus on their humble origins. Sir Eardley Holland was the son of a rural vicar and Sir George Godber's dad was a market gardener in Bedford. This hardly amounts to being raised by wolves but it will have to do.

The back story

We'll be on firmer ground in the years leading up to the CEMD, when women were fighting to be heard. Maternal mortality was a national scandal in the 1920s and the Ministry of Health formed an all-female team to tackle it. They were led by one of Britain's pioneering women doctors, Janet Campbell, daughter of a Brighton bank manager. She wrote influential reports and became a Dame – and she worked the system. In those days public protest meant holding mass meetings, not waving placards at the cameras, and at the largest of those gatherings in 1928 a message was read from the Queen. She wanted action and was surprisingly familiar with Dame Janet's recommendations. The effect on the government was electric.

In 1930 it published the *Interim Report of the Departmental Committee on Maternal Mortality and Morbidity.* This too could have done with a snappier title but nonetheless it passed into legend as the prototype of the CEMD. Copies are now impossible to find but when I arrived in Leeds in 1990 there was one in the professorial bookcase. Thank goodness it survived my clear-out. It has passages underlined by one of my predecessors and still packs a punch at the age of 91. Dame Janet did a great job.

Arnold and Joe

She remains an elusive figure but some personalities come alive in the archives. Joe Wrigley (the inventor of Wrigley's forceps) was one of the two obstetricians who wrote the first CEMD Report, covering 1952-54. The other was Arnold Walker. Despite being London-based they were down-to-earth northerners and according to George Godber "it was largely due to trust in Arnold and Joe that the Enquiry was accepted". Godber had been very anxious but "public acceptance of the honesty and value of the profession's intentions soon allayed that."

The honesty has been maintained ever since and the CEMD is still trusted by an increasingly cynical public. It surely deserves to have a book written about it. Our proposal has been sent to reviewers. Fingers crossed! I hope I haven't invoked the curse of *"And Finally"* by telling you about it too soon.

[Happily, the reviewers were kind. See page 247.]

Small world?

January again, and my first task is to put the travel plans into the diary. This year it doesn't take long. Zoom has removed the need to travel to meetings, and worry about carbon emissions has stopped us flying. Looking at my old diaries I'm amazed at how much time I spent rushing around for professional reasons. Should I feel guilty about what I did to the planet?

Perhaps, but I was part of a tradition of medical travel going back to William Harvey and beyond. Harvey, a Kentish lad, gained his MD in Padua in 1602, when Italy was Europe's centre of learning. The centre shifted as the years passed but travel remained essential to the development of medicine, including our specialty.

Early role models

William Smellie, the "master of British midwifery", travelled from Lanark to Paris to learn his craft before settling in London in 1740. Elizabeth Nihel, his midwife rival, also studied at Paris's Hotel Dieu. She was a Londoner with French parents so she probably felt at home. Smellie's Scottish accent would have gone down better in Paris than it did in London.

Florence Nightingale, born in Tuscany in 1820, toured Europe as a teenager and visited Abu Simbel as a young woman. Her work in Scutari made her a media celebrity. If she hadn't crossed the Bosporus she might never have revolutionised nursing.

Britain's first female medical students were called the "Edinburgh Seven" but only one of them was from Scotland. Five were from the south of England and one was from Ireland. After being banned from graduating in Edinburgh in 1869, most of them travelled to Europe to graduate, learning the necessary language on the way.

By that time France and Germany were the centres of medical enlightenment. The first issue of *BJOG* in 1902 (when it was the *Journal of Obstetrics and Gynaecology of the British Empire*) devoted 30 pages to summaries of papers from abroad – 17 from France, 13 from Germany and two from the USA.

20th century travellers

The European influence on gynaecology continued in the 20th century. In 1965 my former colleague Archie Crompton travelled through the Iron Curtain to Dresden to learn colposcopy, which had been practised in Germany since the 1920s. He then started a clinic in Manchester and helped Joe Jordan and Albert Singer (of Birmingham and London respectively) to found a British society, the BSCCP, in 1972.

Patrick Steptoe brought laparoscopy to Britain after visiting its pioneers, Raoul Palmer in Paris and Hans Frangenheim in Wuppertal. His 1967 book, *Laparoscopy in Gynaecology*, with a chapter on infertility written by Frangenheim, initiated a new era in UK practice. Steptoe, born in Oxford and trained in London, had moved to Oldham to find a consultant post. In the 1970s Robert Edwards and his colleague Jean Purdy drove there from Cambridge every Friday for seven years before they achieved success with IVF.

Personal experience

My own travelling was less spectacular but essential to my career. It included a pilgrimage to Queen Charlotte's Hospital for the MRCOG course, and a midwinter drive from Edinburgh to Bristol to complete the giant leap from registrar to senior registrar (SR). That was in January 1979, when the temperature in Scotland fell to minus 26.8°C. I was happy to leave.

Only after moving did I realise how much practice varied across the UK. Having gone south of Manchester I had to be taught vaginal hysterectomy – an embarrassing experience for an SR. Travel broadened the mind but involved difficult decisions for doctors who were married to doctors. Some couples met only at weekends for several years. Looking back, my wife and I tell ourselves we're glad we moved, and our children seemed to enjoy the variety.

The perils of staying put

Trainees now have the stability of "run-through" training – a phrase that suggests something easier than our uphill slog. A glance at the RCOG's 62-page Core Curriculum corrects that impression. Its standards of skill and empathy are so high that my generation could achieve them only in our obituaries. And now that world-class teaching is available online, trainees can meet them without leaving home. But I still worry. Will cabin fever be added to burnout on the list of occupational diseases affecting consultants? Surely they'll need to get out and mix. They should visit colleagues in Europe, as our predecessors did. It might well be a learning experience and it would be one in the eye for the Brexiteers.

Doctor Short

Why doesn't *TOG* have an obituary column? I ask because my MD supervisor died last July and the news didn't reach me until January. I feel aggrieved that nobody told me. It's an irrational feeling but I think many of my generation will sympathise.

The answer, of course, is that *TOG* is a journal of medical education, and obituaries are none of their business. But they used to be, years ago. In 1951, according to Pubmed, the world's medical journals published 1408 obituaries. That was a post-war peak, reflecting an era when nations needed heroes, and not only on the battlefield. As time passed, however, the mood changed. We now prefer to read about rogues. The last obituary in *BJOG* was in 1971 (78:191-2) and in 2021 the total in Pubmed was 38. Doctors no longer celebrate their predecessors, and I think that's a shame.

All creatures great and small

Actually my MD supervisor, Roger Short, wasn't a doctor. He qualified as a vet but turned to science and was elected a Fellow of the Royal Society in 1974, shortly after arriving in Edinburgh to lead the then-new MRC Unit of Reproductive Biology. I was a very junior doctor and was quick to knock on his door asking for a research project. He suggested the normal human breast "because nobody else was working on it". The resulting papers attracted a mixture of hilarity and outrage but I eventually got my MD.

The MRC Unit also studied reproduction in animals – from mice to marmosets to red deer – and some of Roger's early work had been on contraception in elephants. At his interview for the Edinburgh post he'd been asked: "Wouldn't we be better to appoint a doctor?" and he cheekily answered: "Yes". As things turned out, his broad perspective was just what that new field of research needed.

He was "Dr Short" in those days but gained a Personal Chair before emigrating to Australia in 1982. His Englishness and mischievous ideas went down well there and he became a national scientific celebrity. I have a photo of him and Sir David Attenborough chatting in Melbourne about elephants. He died there at the age of 91, mourned by many former research fellows like me, but his only UK obituary is in *Twin Research and Human Genetics* (2021;24(4):241-3). Scientific journals still celebrate scientists.

The performing gene

I heard the news when a friend sent me a link to an Australian journal called *Cosmos*. A good obituary always tells you something you didn't know, even about an old friend, and I discovered that Roger's mother had been an actress. She organised weekly play readings for her children and this, he said, was how he "learned how to hold an audience". Ah yes, that fits. His talks always seemed relaxed but listeners would emerge from seminar room or auditorium wide-eyed and inspired.

He tried to show me how it was done. "Always know what your next slide is, Jim, and lead up to it". This was long before PowerPoint presentations arrived to fill the screen with CGI effects and bewilder the audience. And I remember the first manuscript I showed him. I fancied myself as a writer and it was a shock to get it back covered in corrections. Today I still see those arrows in red ink as I shuffle my on-screen paragraphs.

Hell's gynaecologists

Do such recollections interest the general reader? That's what editors ask as they try to juggle too many doctors and not enough space. The *BMJ* has wrestled with this problem for years and now publishes paragraphs with little more than the name of the deceased and the terminal diagnosis (even nonagenarians aren't allowed to die of old age). Fortunately the online versions are better.

Some years ago the *BMJ* invited readers to file self-written obituaries. There were few takers but I submitted mine and it was published. It told how I and other retirees had formed an over-70s motorcycle display team called "Hell's gynaecologists". I was stood at the top of the pyramid when it all ended in a grisly pile-up.

Sadly, humour too has disappeared from medical journals. It seems unlikely to return but I hope obituaries make a comeback. Teaching is still done by people, not guidelines, and teachers need role models and a bit of encouragement. Most of us doctors remember someone who, like Roger, changed our lives and whom we were too shy to thank. It's only polite to do so, even belatedly.

Room 101

Last March the Retired Fellows and Members Society (RFMS) made its first in-person visit to 10 Union Street. We were impressed. The atrium is an inspiring space, with its white spiral staircase soaring to the top floor. We resisted the challenge and took the lift to our meeting in Room 101. The name sounded ominous. On television *"Room 101"* was a cellar for celebrities' pet hates, and before that it was the torture chamber in George Orwell's novel *1984*. He named it after the place where the BBC held management meetings.

The RCOG's version is much more inviting and we enjoyed catching up with our contemporaries. We have similar interests, memories and symptoms, and best of all we're no longer in a rush. Nobody was bleeped and hardly anyone was phoned. The RFMS, founded more than twenty years ago, is open to all retired Fellows and Members. The limiting factor was the need to travel to London but that changed during lockdown, when our first online meeting attracted a global attendance of several hundred.

The B word

Like all doctors we'd retired at an average age of 60. That's when other professionals are reaching their prime. Judges and magistrates retire at 75. Baroness Hale was appointed President of the Supreme Court at 72. The Rolling Stones (average age 76) are planning a European tour. So what's medicine's problem? Some call it "burnout", a term that first appeared in the 1970s when it was applied to nurses. Last year burnout was the subject of 3468 papers in Pubmed but, like "neurasthenia" in the 19th century, it's an unhelpful label. None of us retirees was burned out. We left because we were sick of being undervalued.

Time to go, boys

The campaign to undermine consultants began forty years ago when medicine was still a patriarchy and doctors were seen as all-powerful. In 1980, BBC Radio's Reith Lectures, *Unmasking Medicine*, urged listeners to take back control. The lecturer, Ian Kennedy (later Sir Ian), caught the public mood but I thought he was on another planet. I was a senior registrar in Bristol and when I drove to the labour ward in the wee small hours I felt anything but powerful.

I came to Leeds in the 1990s and so did the Department of Health. This meant I could overhear civil servants' conversations on the London train. I was surprised by their contempt for senior doctors, but I shouldn't have been. *The Times* kept saying that we spent most of our time on the golf course. The NHS saw us as an impediment to reform and ousted us from management. And the rise of feminism made male obstetricians a prime target. Buzz off, guys, childbirth is women's business.

When we left, the hurt faded but last week it came back to me with a bang. A colleague sent me a video of a talk I'd given in 2009 just after I retired. She'd found it during her own pre-retirement clear-out and it had struck a chord. Wide-eyed, I watched my 62-year-old self showing slides of the National Childbirth Trust's snide insults and the "normal birth" movement's idealistic hyperbole. I sounded surprisingly bitter. My generation had helped make pregnancy safe and now we were surplus to requirements.

A forgotten report

Why am I telling you this? Well, at our March meeting the RFMS discussed the latest UK childbirth safety scandal and asked why the College hadn't done more to prevent it. I explained the zeitgeist of the 1990s and said that the College, like King Canute, knew it was hopeless to try holding back the tide. But the video reminded me that we did our best. In 1999 RCOG and RCM published a consensus plan, *Towards Safer Childbirth*, in which labour wards would be staffed by senior doctors – the hours depending on the hospital's total number of births. The recommendation was repeated in 2007 and 2008, supported by four Royal Colleges. NHS mandarins responded with chicanery. Births in midwife-led areas would not be counted because they were "low risk". Today *Towards Safer Childbirth* is available on Amazon at an eye-watering £747.92p (very few copies must have escaped shredding).

Back to the future?

Aside from setting the record straight, have I any suggestions? Could we reinvent a medical career structure which incorporates the voice of experience? Banishing the over-60s to Room 101 hasn't improved things as much as the NHS hoped. But no, that's enough from me for now. I'm off to plan a European tour.

Road to recovery

Over the last two years I've tried to avoid mentioning Covid by name but you may have noticed its effects on this column.   At first they were insidious.   In April 2020 this page had a review of *The Welkin*, a play about attitudes to women in the 18th century.   I urged readers to go and see it but on 17th March the National Theatre was hit by lockdown and my recommendation was deleted before *TOG's* presses rolled.   An easy change for us, but not for the 18 actors (most of them women) who were suddenly thrown out of work.

Later in 2020 I documented my discovery of Zoom as a medium for lectures and – less successfully – for after-dinner speeches.   And I lamented the fact that *This Medical Life*, a book of my collected *BMJ* columns, had to be launched without any glitzy parties or personal appearances in bookshops. Nonetheless a small advertisement in *The Oldie* propelled it briefly up to the 23,000s on Amazon's best-seller list.   My publisher was delighted and has asked me to remind you that it's still in print.

Joking for gerries

In July 2021 I wrote optimistically about an upcoming 50-year reunion of Edinburgh medical graduates.   In October I mentioned that it had been cancelled.   The disappointment was short-lived and we're planning a joint 1970/71 jubilee this autumn.   It could get emotional.   Face-to-face meetings have a special atmosphere after two years of lockdown, particularly at our age when not everyone has survived the long wait.

Our two-man cabaret for the reunion is still going ahead.   The average age of performers and audience is now 75, which, strangely, feels very different from being 74.   Walter, my musical partner, and I are taking a long hard look at jokes which have become old friends over the years. Most of them are facing the axe and we're editing our songs to take account of modern sensitivities.   Self-mockery is safe ground but there are only so many jokes you can make about getting old.   The word "geriatric" now has a black box in the *Oxford English Dictionary* saying it's likely to cause offence.

Happily, we've got several new songs. At Walter's suggestion I've written medical lyrics to Billy Joel's *We didn't light the fire,* which lists key events in American history between 1949 and 1989.   It's a brilliant idea and Walter assures me the audience will recognise the tune. I'm unconvinced. I prefer classical music and it was a relief when a classmate said he was looking forward to hearing our 1971 hit, *The ward round,* to the tune of JS Bach's *Jesu, Joy of Man's Desiring.* Both songs will be fun to perform – which, of course, is why we're doing the show.

On a mission

Similarly, the book I mentioned here in October 2021 was written because my co-authors and I wanted to do it, not because we had to. Thanks to the internet, historical research is the ideal lockdown activity and it was a lightbulb moment when I realised that nobody had written the story of the *Confidential Enquiries into Maternal Deaths.* Our book was accepted by Cambridge University Press and is now at the printers, but it has evolved into something much more than a history book.

It now has international contributors and a foreword by Professor Mahmoud Fathalla, the great champion of women's childbirth rights. He quotes Winston Churchill: "The longer you can look back, the farther you can look forward". The book's title is *Why Mothers Died and How Their Lives are Saved,* and the second half has grown in importance. Another foreword by Donna Ockenden discusses public disquiet about routine maternity care in the UK and draws parallels with the early years of the CEMD. Our predecessors solved similar problems and this book describes how they did it.

My co-authors and I have become filled with missionary zeal to spread the news. A lecture tour perhaps? I'm thinking about a talk called *"Forgotten Heroines – and Heroes".* It would be ...

Listen to t' people

My typing has been interrupted by the Property Maintenance Specialist (formerly odd-job man) working on our ageing house. He's discovered that I'm a doctor and he has forthright views on the state of the NHS. "I'll tell you what they need to do," he says. "They need to put t'doctors back in charge." I gaze at him with renewed respect. How did he gain such insight without reading our book?

Obstetricians and midwives: an embarrassing history

Recently the Royal Society of Medicine ran a series of webinars on the history of surgery. One was about gynaecology and obstetrics. Carolyn Paul from London discussed the chequered past of gynaecological surgery and did a great job. I followed with the history of obstetrics. It's a subject I've written a lot about but with a limit of 35 minutes I needed to take a fresh look at the big picture. It produced some surprises.

Historical names

One was realising that I'd lived through most of the major advances. Ultrasound transformed practice while I was a junior doctor in the 1970s. The original 1958 paper, from Glasgow, was by Donald, MacVicar and Brown – all of whom I later met. And I'd met Sir Dugald Baird after his pioneering work on women's health in Aberdeen. In 1979 I attended Kieran O'Driscoll's controversial course in Dublin on preventing prolonged labour. And I knew Iain Chalmers, who was inspired by Archie Cochrane in Cardiff to develop evidence-based obstetrics. Take care, I told myself. Avoid celebrity name-dropping, and try not to point out that all those innovations came from the Celtic fringe.

The next surprise was discovering the significance of the word "obstetrics". The Oxford English Dictionary says it entered the language in 1813. Before that, obstetricians were "man midwives". William Smellie's 1752 textbook was *A Treatise on the Practice of Midwifery,* and Scottish professors from James Young Simpson onwards (including Dugald Baird and Ian Donald) held *Chairs of Midwifery,* not obstetrics. But in the early 19th century doctors (all male, of course) wanted to differentiate themselves from female birth attendants who had been denied university education. The men gave themselves the Latin name for "midwife", creating a false impression that our specialty has classical roots.

I could see why. By 1813 the "man-midwife" had become a figure of fun. I showed Isaac Cruikshank's 1793 cartoon of a hermaphrodite figure – half-man with instruments behind him, and half-woman at a cosy fireside (google "Cruikshank man midwife"). It's not just a historical curiosity. It illustrates the eternal dilemma of maternity care – to intervene or not to intervene? – and the fact that for centuries it was gender-based.

Three hundred years of forceps

Obstetric forceps were introduced by the man-midwives of the 18th century after the Chamberlen family finally released its trade secret. Widely misused, forceps soon fell out of fashion, but after the deaths of Princess Charlotte and her baby (and the suicide of her non-interventionist obstetrician) in 1817, they became part of a doctor's stock-in-trade. For a century after the introduction of anaesthesia in 1847, obstetricians regarded caesarean section as a shameful failure.

Obstetricians of my generation, the last to be adept with Kielland's, were proud of their skills and only dimly aware of the harm done by forceps during home deliveries. Until the late 1930s, domiciliary midwives were not allowed to give pain relief and had to call the family doctor, who had had only undergraduate training. Ill-advised use of forceps helped maintain the UK maternal mortality rate at Victorian levels until 1935.

The darkest hour - and the dawn?

Teaching midwives about analgesia was a seismic change. For a century doctors had vetoed the training of their financial competitors. When the London Obstetrical Society introduced a midwifery diploma in 1872, doctors threatened to report the president to the GMC. In the mid-20th century midwives chafed at being seen as specialist nurses, and when feminism grew in the 1980s they decided to shake off their "doctors' handmaidens" image. In 1993 the Health Department's *Changing Childbirth* report widened the gulf between us, and in 2005 the RCM's "Campaign for Normal Birth" made non-intervention the aim of maternity units across the country, setting the scene for today's maternity scandals.

My talk might have ended there but fortunately I was updated by the RCOG Retired Fellows and Members Society. In December Gill Walton, the RCM Chief Executive, spoke to us about the new "One Voice" policy of both colleges, made easier by their sharing the same building . Inspired, I discovered the British Intrapartum Care Society, founded in 2018, a specialist association where it's hard to tell the midwives from the obstetricians.

What a pleasure to have good news to end not only my talk but also this, my 96th (and final) column for *TOG*. In one of my last *BMJ* columns (2013;346:f2214) I tried to imagine how we'd all see ourselves in 25 years' time: "Separate royal colleges for midwives and obstetricians? Really??" Well, a man can dream.

Index